Something in Martyn's voice had Helen's eyes jerking back to his face, and a quiver ran through her as she met his look.

'The house is empty, Martyn,' she told him chillingly. 'There's nothing for you here now.'

'On the contrary, I've already discovered more than I bargained for!'

'Uncle Gerald is dead!' Now his eyes were two dark pinpricks of light as he watched her.

'You still use your childhood name for him,' he declared softly. 'It always used to make me think we were related in some way, Helen. That there was a bond between us——'

'There's nothing between us!' she snapped, then stopped abruptly, checking herself, struggling to retain the shreds of her composure under that unnerving stare. 'Why have you come?'

MILLS & BOON LIMITED
17–19 FOLEY STREET, LONDON W1A 1DR

SAYTON'S FOLLY

BY

PAMELA HATTON

MILLS & BOON LIMITED
ETON HOUSE   18–24 PARADISE ROAD
RICHMOND   SURREY   TW9 1SR

First published in Great Britain 1990
by Mills & Boon Limited

© Pamela Hatton 1990

Australian copyright 1990
Philippine copyright 1990
This edition 1990

ISBN 0 263 76866 X

Set in 10 on 11½ pt Linotron Times
01-9011-51769
Typeset in Great Britain by Centracet, Cambridge
Made and printed in Great Britain

CHAPTER ONE

'. . .AND SO you see, my dear, there's nothing else for it.'

Helen stared, white-faced, at the solicitor. 'You mean—we'll have to *leave*?'

'I'm afraid so.'

'But—but it's our *home*!'

The break in her voice on the last word made Mr Winstanley of Winstanley and Barker shuffle the papers in front of him uncomfortably, and Helen swallowed painfully, bringing her teeth down hard on her lip to stop it trembling.

'Are you sure they know the facts?' she got out in more controlled tones. 'Are you sure they understand our circumstances? That my mother——?'

'The instructions from the London solicitors are very precise,' Mr Winstanley interrupted gently. 'I'm afraid the matter has been taken out of my hands.' He handed a letter across the desk as he spoke and Helen's eyes skimmed over the embossed heading, elegantly inscribed with the impressive name of a London legal firm, and down over the pristinely typed paragraphs. It was brief, but, as he'd said, very precise. Almost abruptly so. 'The Lodge must be vacated within six weeks.' That sentence seemed to burn into her mind like a neon sign.

She handed the letter back, and his own mouth compressed as he glanced at it before placing it neatly back on the pile.

He had known Helen Ashley, as she was now, for

most of her life, and as he looked at her shining, shoulder-length blonde hair and shaded blue eyes it was hard for him to think of her as anything but the child she had once been, even though she must now be well into her twenties, and with a child of her own into the bargain. But her waif-like figure was thinner than ever, and who could wonder? The poor child had had enough to cope with these last few months, what with the death of her mother not six weeks ago, and now this. . .

He adjusted his glasses and stood up to come round the desk and take Helen's hand, patting it abstractedly. 'I'm sorry, my dear, but there's nothing more I can do.' But Helen was in control of herself again now. She straightened in her chair and managed a brief, taut smile.

'You've already done more than enough.'

'I wish I could do more.' He squeezed her hand. 'Try to look on the bright side, my dear. At least you have six weeks, which is something you didn't have before.'

'Yes.' Helen agreed, nodding, and her hair danced round her face, sending out reflected lights of red and gold. Six weeks! Six weeks in which to find another home. Six weeks in which to pack up most of her life, and not only hers, but Jamie's too. . .

At the thought of her son she stood up abruptly.

'Well, thank you for letting me know so quickly,' she murmured, and gently withdrew her hand.

'You will let me know how you get on?' he asked. She nodded again, and his aged lips compressed in anger against those unseen forces in London.

'Goodbye.'

Outside on the pavement Helen stood dazed and desolate. Six weeks! She closed her eyes in a brief moment of despair. If only Simon were here, she thought bleakly. He would know what to do!

But Simon wasn't here, and if he was, she wouldn't be in this mess in the first place, she told herself firmly. No, there was only herself now, herself and Jamie, and she had to think for both of them. And think she would, she was sure of that. Something would turn up—it had to! She had Jamie to think of, and he was her life. She would fight for his happiness—tooth and nail if necessary! And as Mr Winstanley had said, at least now she knew she had those six precious weeks. . .

She turned left from Winstanley and Barker and began to walk briskly along the main street of Kingsleigh. It was a fine June morning and the small market town was busy with Saturday morning shoppers. Helen gave a brief glance at her watch and quickened her pace, dodging lightly along the crowded pavement, oblivious of glances from the occasional male eye. She was not a tall girl, but her slim figure, topped by that shining mass of hair, drew many a masculine look; but Helen remained completely unaware, her thoughts firmly fixed on her young son.

Jamie was at Kingsleigh's one and only leisure centre having his usual Saturday morning swimming lesson; not that he needed lessons—he was already an excellent swimmer. He was learning how to improve his style and technique over greater distances, and he loved it, loved the fierce competition with other boys of his age. Despite his youth, Helen had already caught glimpses of the raw masculinity, the long-limbed athleticism that had been his father's. . .

She stopped abruptly at the edge of the pavement, looking right and left with a hiss of impatience as she realised she would have to wait for a break in the traffic before she could cross the road.

At one time she would never even have allowed herself to look for signs of his father in Jamie, but these last couple of years especially, as Jamie grew older, taller, she had occasionally caught a look, a gesture, that had sent a pang of awareness through her. . . She darted across the road, ignoring the blare of a horn as, with another glance at her watch, she swung through the gates of the leisure centre and took a short cut across the grass. Jamie would be out of the water now, perhaps already changed—and even as she pushed through the glass double doors into the foyer she heard a shout and Jamie was coming towards her, the blond hair that exactly matched her own darkened and spiked with dampness, his towel clutched in front of him and a grin from ear to ear.

'Hi, Mum. Peter's mum gave me money for crisps.'

'Oh, she did, did she?' Helen stopped, catching her breath as Jamie covered the remaining distance between them. She couldn't help but smile at the look on his face. He hardly ever had anything out of the machines in the foyer; she considered them too expensive, and he knew it.

'It's a "thank you" for bringing Peter home from school for me last week,' Liz Thompson told her as she came up behind Jamie, her own son in tow. 'I knew they'd both be hungry after swimming, and I wasn't sure how long you'd be, so. . .' She shrugged, smiling, but her eyes were fixed on Helen's strained features.

'Thanks, Liz,' Helen returned, greeting her friend, 'and for looking after Jamie for me. I didn't realise it would take so long.'

'How did it go?' Liz asked. They had turned to

follow the two boys out to the car park, but her eyes were still fixed intently on Helen.

'It's as I feared,' Helen said briefly, and the look on Liz's face altered completely.

'You have to leave? Oh, Helen, that's too much! After all your mother did for the old man—and now you're being turned on to the streets like—like beggars! It's disgraceful!'

'There's nothing we can do,' Helen echoed hollowly, and looked up then, meeting Liz's look, warning her to be careful of what she said in front of Jamie. The two boys were swinging through the double doors now, but if they hadn't been so engrossed in each other it would have been perfectly possible for them to hear what was being said.

'You still haven't said anything to him?' Liz asked in a lower tone, and Helen shook her head.

'There was no point, not until I knew for certain. . .'

'You'll appeal, of course?'

'Oh, Liz, we haven't got a leg to stand on!' It was difficult now to keep the desperation out of her voice, and Liz's mouth compressed even further.

'But it's so unfair! Your family have lived there for years——'

'That's the whole point, Liz. My mother was the official tenant, not me.'

'But they're letting us stay on at the farm——'

'That's probably because you pay your rent—on the nail!'

'But your mother was a special case!' Liz persisted. 'Everyone knows that. She was more like a member of the family than a housekeeper—and after all she did for Gerald Sayton—good heavens, it's thanks to her he lived as long as he did! No one else could have put up with his eccentricities—or his temper! Your mother may not have paid any rent, Helen, but we all know what Gerald's wages were like, and if she hadn't had you to support her——!'

'My mother is dead, Liz,' Helen interrupted tautly. 'And so is Uncle Gerald; and now Sayton's Folly belongs to the London side of the family. You've only lived in Penford a relatively short time—you have no idea what the London Saytons are like!' And now it was impossible to keep the intensity out of her voice. Even the thought of any of that grasping, avaricious family coming to the Folly—taking Gerald's place— left her with a bitter, burning sense of injustice!

Liz must have caught the sudden shift of emotion, for she looked up. 'I know Gerald wouldn't have anything to do with any of them,' she responded, eyeing the two dark patches of colour coming into Helen's face. 'But then, he was like that with everyone. Surely they can't all be as bad as he liked to make out?'

'I thought that once,' Helen muttered fiercely, and then stopped on a harsh, indrawn breath as a picture of a forceful masculine face with dark hair and penetrating grey eyes suddenly flashed into her mind, but she pushed it firmly away. All that had died a long time ago, along with her heart! Oh, yes, she had once foolishly thought, as Liz did now, that because of what Gerald's brother had done to him, Gerald had tarred all the rest of his family with the same brush! In her innocence she had been as gullible as the rest—but she had learned her lesson the hard way. In the end she had been the biggest fool of all!

She realised suddenly that Liz was still watching her, her eyes startled, surprised, and with an effort Helen pulled herself together. It was a long time since she had allowed herself to become so emotional—and now twice in the same day!

'I think, in a way, I'm already resigned to leaving,' she got out in a taut voice. 'It's what I've half feared all along, and now that it's actually happened I've just got to accept it!'

'Well, if it comes to the crunch, you can always come to us until you find a place of your own,' Liz soothed. 'That is—if you don't mind sharing with Jamie——?'

'Thanks, Liz.' Surprised and touched, Helen managed a brief smile, but even as she added warmly, 'That's very kind of you,' she knew she could never take up Liz's offer. Hall Farm was bursting at the seams as it was, without her and Jamie to add to the mêlée. She'd known Liz ever since she and her husband had taken over Hall Farm from Simon's parents when they had gone to Australia to join their other son, and she knew how open-hearted Liz was, but these days she seemed to wear an air of constant hassle. Whether the farm wasn't doing as well as it should, or whether it was something more personal— Liz's mother-in-law had just come to live with them after being forced to sell her own farm in Somerset— Helen wasn't sure, but she knew one thing. She could never live at Hall Farm. It held too many memories— memories of a past she had tried so hard to forget.

'Thanks, Liz,' she said again. 'But no, thanks. Hall Farm was Simon's old home.'

'Of course—how stupid of me to forget! I'm sorry. . .' Liz's face was a picture of remorse as she touched Helen's arm. 'But then, it is over six years ago now, Helen. I'm surprised you've never. . .'

She faltered to a halt, watching Helen's face, probing curiosity vying with the uncertainty in her eyes, but Helen was giving nothing away this time. She was silent, her eyes veiled by their long lashes, and after a moment Liz reverted abruptly to her original topic.

'Well, the offer's still open if you change your mind—and you're always welcome, Helen, you know that. In any case, you'll still be bringing Jamie to the party this afternoon? Peter is thrilled to bits that he's staying overnight.'

'Of course,' Helen looked over to where Jamie now stood in the middle of the car park. He had already said goodbye to Peter and was looking impatiently in her direction. 'He wouldn't miss it for the world,' she said. 'Four-thirty?'

'Four-thirty,' Liz agreed, and looked quickly at her watch. 'Oh, lord! I've just remembered the cake!' she exclaimed, and with a hurried 'I'll see you later!' she dashed across to her car, calling abstractedly to her son.

Helen turned and walked more slowly across to where Jamie was waiting by their own battered Ford. She'd left it here while she'd walked to the solicitors. Now she could see Rags, their woolly-haired mongrel, leaping excitedly about inside it, and almost before she'd unlocked the door Jamie had dived into the back seat to meet an ecstatic reception fron his pet.

'It's all right, boy—we're going home now!' she heard him say, and, as she watched him tussle laughingly with the dog, her heart lurched.

How on earth am I going to tell him? she thought, as she slid into the driver's seat and put the key in the ignition with fingers that trembled. How on earth am I going to tell him that the place we call home is no longer ours?

*   *   *

The village of Penford was about five miles outside Kingsleigh, although it could hardly be called a village; it was more a collection of houses with a pub and a post office, but beyond it, by just over two miles, lay Sayton's Folly, and just before that, tucked into a slight bend in the road, the Lodge.

Helen had lived at the Lodge all her life, except for the two brief years of her marriage to Simon, and as she drove down the familiar road with Jamie humming tunelessly to himself in the back seat, her heightened senses seemed doubly aware of the countryside around her. These were the trees, the fields, the hedges she had known all her life, and today even the grass seemed to shimmer, brilliantly green in the sunshine. She drove round the final bend and there was the Lodge, set in its own secluded corner. The cottage garden that her mother had always kept so neatly stretched down to the woods on one side, and the tall iron gates of the Folly on the other, and it was through these gates that Helen now drove, but instead of continuing up the drive she turned off to pull in behind the Lodge, and with a shriek of glee Jamie was out of the car and racing across the back lawn, Rags at his heels, towards the ramshackle old den he and Helen and Sarah, her mother, had built last summer. Helen was left standing by the car, a smile touching the corners of her mouth as she watched him go. But then the smile faded.

Jamie loved this place as much as she did, but his was the more simplistic love of a child. This was the only home he had ever known. His young mind had never even considered what it would be like to live anywhere else, whereas she—she had far more complex emotions concerning this place. Her whole life was bound up here; her laughter, her tears, her sweetheart, her lover. . .

She closed her eyes on a ragged sigh, the conversation with Liz still fresh in her mind. No one had any idea of the tortuous emotions even the very name of Sayton still had the power to arouse in her. . .

'Martyn,' she whispered.

She could even say his name now without that terrible pain around her heart. At one time she had tried to shut him out of her life completely, refusing even to think about him, but these last months, while Gerald had been so ill, he had gradually crept back into her consciousness. At first she had been half afraid he would return to Sayton's Folly, but there had been so sign of him, not even a word, and gradually she had begun to relax again. But now, with Gerald's death—and her mother's so close behind—all that had changed, and suddenly everything was simmering dangerously close to the surface again, and her only relief now was that Sarah wasn't here to hear some of the gossip.

Her mouth twisted wryly. People in the village knew almost as much about the Sayton's fated history as she did herself—or at least, they thought they did! They could only guess, speculate on wild rumours of what had happened that fateful summer nine years ago. Even Liz would probably be shocked if she knew the truth. That Jamie wasn't really Simon's son, that in reality he was a Sayton. . .

She leaned her hot face against the cool glass of the car for a moment, and her eyes caught the line of the drive as it wound its way for almost a quarter of a mile to where Sayton's Folly itself stood, just visible through the trees.

At least the house itself had remained constant, she

thought hollowly. It stood as it had stood for well over a hundred years, its red-brick façade and mullioned windows gazing serenely out over the fertile Cheshire countryside; but now even that too could be under threat. It was assumed that Gerald's brother, Richard Sayton, was taking it over, and who knew what his feelings were about this beautiful old place? The burning question was, would he sell it?

At least there were no worries now about Martyn returning! Helen thought savagely. His main reason for coming here in the first place had been to get away from Richard, his father, and if he hadn't had the decency to come and see Gerald when he had been ill—dying—then he certainly wouldn't come now! And she turned abruptly to slam the car door shut and walk round to pull her shopping bags and Jamie's damp swimming gear out of the boot.

Even before Gerald's death, she had had her doubts about the security of her and her mother's future at the Lodge, but Sarah had remained completely unruffled.

'Whatever happens, it won't make any difference to us,' Helen remembered her saying firmly. 'We'll continue to live at the Lodge. It will be ours then. Gerald told me so—he's put it in his will.'

But who else would put their trust in a man known for his eccentricities and already on his deathbed? No one, it seemed, not even Mr Winstanley, and he had known Uncle Gerald himself. But then, he was a solicitor and he dealt in facts, and Sarah was dead now too, and though the house had been searched from top to bottom, no will had been found, and from the moment Richard Sayton's name had first been mentioned, Helen had known she wouldn't be allowed to stay.

She stuffed Jamie's damp towel into one of the bulging carrier bags with unnecessary force. It was just that she had never expected her dismissal to come in such a cold and callous fashion! And once again she felt a strange kind of relief that at least Sarah wasn't here to know what was happening, for if by some miracle she could have survived her heart attack six weeks ago, the shock of knowing she had to leave Sayton's Folly would surely have given her another one.

To be fair, Helen argued as she slammed the boot down and gathered up the bags from the path, they had paid hardly any rent since her father had died when she had been small. Sarah's reduced income had been barely enough for them to live on, but Gerald had hated the thought of having to find another housekeeper—he'd hated any kind of change on the estate—and Sarah had been heartbroken at the thought of leaving this place she loved, so Gerald had waived the rent.

Sarah had paid him back in other ways. She had always been active and hardworking, and these last ten years or so she had virtually devoted her life to looking after the old man, despite his idiosyncratic ways. His increasingly uncertain temper and dislike of strangers had made him into a virtual recluse these last two years, and Sarah had been almost his only contact with the outside world.

But now her mother's loyalty to Gerald counted for nothing—especially with his brother, the man he had hated!

'It's facts that count, Helen,' Mr Winstanley had told her. 'And the fact is there's no record of any rent being paid these last few years. And if it is decided to sell the Lodge, that debt to the estate would be repaid many times over. Country cottages are in great demand these days.'

And who could blame Richard Sayton, feeling as he must do about Sayton's Folly, about *her*, from cashing in on that demand?

Still, it seemed a cruel irony that Gerald should have spent his life struggling to keep the remains of the estate together, only to have it fall to pieces after his death!

Helen let herself into the kitchen and dumped the bags on the kitchen floor, before straightening to stare bleakly round the familiar room.

She still hadn't got used to how empty the house felt, how unnaturally quiet it seemed when Jamie wasn't in. She kept thinking she would turn round and Sarah would be there, smiling that whimsical, mischievous smile that always meant she had been up to something and was enjoying some private joke of her own. Jamie was missing his grandmother too, she could tell. They had been so close. And Sarah would have known, too, exactly how to break the news to Jamie that soon they would have to leave this place. That soon he would no longer have the fields and the woods and the stream to play in. That soon they might not even have a garden. . .

With a heavy sigh Helen threw her handbag down on to the kitchen table, and her jacket after it, and walked slowly out through the kitchen door again and across the lawn to find Jamie.

That night she lay tossing and turning in the darkness, unable to get to sleep, the day's events going round and round in despairing circles in her head.

She'd told Jamie, as she had known she must. After all, there had been no point in putting it off any longer, and, as she had feared, Jamie had been at first stunned, and then adamant that he didn't want to leave.

'I like it here!' he had declared defiantly, and then, echoing her own words to Mr Winstanley, 'It's our home!'

And so, as simply as she could, she had explained why they had to go.

'But this man—Uncle Gerald's brother—doesn't even know us!' Jamie had countered fiercely, his chin wobbling ominously. 'When he meets us he might like us—he might want us to stay——!'

'*I doubt it!*' Helen had interrupted derisively, then had stopped, biting her lip. She had promised herself that she wouldn't involve Jamie in any bitterness from the past—her past. After all, to him the Saytons were simply Gerald's family—unknown, unseen. And to the Saytons he was simply her son—hers and Simon's, and she had no intention of changing any of that. For if they should ever discover the truth. . .if *Martyn* should ever discover the truth. . .

'Uncle Gerald had a falling-out with his brother years ago,' she'd explained, abruptly dragging her thoughts back to Jamie's troubled features, 'and he wasn't on speaking terms with the rest of his London relations either. So you see, Jamie, his brother might not even want to come back to the Folly—he might simply sell it, and even if he did decide to live here, the Folly needs a lot doing to it. Things like the roof being repaired, and windows being replaced. If the Lodge were sold, the money would help pay for all those things.' And then, at the sight of tears in Jamie's eyes, a flash of inspiration had struck her. 'You're always saying that you wish your friends lived a little nearer to you. We could find somewhere where there were children living close by—how would you like that?'

Jamie had wiped his wet cheeks. 'Like in the village?' he had asked, still sniffing.

'Well, perhaps not in the village. . .' she had replied slowly. 'Penford is only small, and besides, there are no houses for sale.'

'What about Kingsleigh?' Jamie had asked hopefully. 'Most of my friends from school live in Kingsleigh.'

'Well, we'll have to see,' Helen had demurred, but she had smiled, relieved to see that he had no longer been looking so worried at the prospect. And Jamie had rambled on, obviously getting over his initial shock. Even when she'd driven him over to Hall Farm later, he had still been talking about it, and that was partly the reason why her heart was so heavy now.

She didn't want him building false hopes. She was terribly afraid she was fooling him and deluding herself.

They might not even be able to afford a house, let alone in Kingsleigh; prices there were exorbitant. She still had the money from the sale of her married home, of course, and, despite the necessity of having to draw lump sums out now and again, the bulk of it remained intact. But what had seemed like an enormous amount of money six years ago now seemed barely enough to cover the deposit on a small terraced cottage—and there was still the question of whether or not her salary as a teacher at Kingsleigh High would cover a mortgage. What if they had to move into town? How would Jamie cope? How would *she* cope?

She closed her eyes on a harsh sigh, remembering the flat she had shared with Simon in Manchester. It had been large and airy and comfortable, but still a flat. There had been no green fields, no trees. She had spent every night dreaming of Sayton's Folly. . .

An unexpected sound suddenly had her eyes jerking open again, and she lay in the darkness, listening. The illuminated dial of her bedside clock told her it was almost two-thirty, and she frowned, then climbed out of bed to pad to the window to look up through the trees towards the Folly.

She thought she'd heard a car—not on the road, but on the drive up to the house; but she'd seen no lights, and she could see nothing now, just the trees waving gently against the night sky. With a hiss of impatience she turned away from the window to stare at the bed, but she didn't climb back into it. She went out to the landing and stood at the top of the stairs, annoyed because she was tired, and yet sleep seemed further away now than ever—and then a sound at the bottom of the stairs told her she wasn't alone.

She peered down into the darkness of the stairwell. 'Hello, Rags, can't you sleep either?' she whispered softly, and went down to him to nuzzle his ears. 'How about a drink, hmm?'

He followed her through to the kitchen. She didn't put the light on; she didn't need to. She knew the kitchen well enough to find her way blindfold.

For the same reason she never drew the curtains. It wasn't necessary—except perhaps at the front during the long winter evenings. After all, there was no one to see, nothing but fields and trees stretching away to the Folly and beyond, and it was towards the Folly that Helen now found herself staring as she filled the kettle at the kitchen sink.

And then suddenly she froze, hand still on the tap.

She'd seen a light—she was sure of it this time. Either a car headlight, or perhaps a powerful torch.

The kettle clattered into the sink as she strained to see, eyes alerted to the slightest flicker, but the light had gone.

She caught her lip between her teeth. What should she do? Call the police?

She thought of John Simpson, the local bobby. Was it worth dragging him out of his bed at this time of night just because she thought she'd seen a light? After all, it might only be a tramp—but then, tramps didn't usually have torches. What if it was burglars?

Everyone for miles around knew about Gerald's death—it had even prompted a write-up in the county paper, and anyone driving past the gates, or seeing the house from a distance, would hardly be expected to know that there was nothing of any value there. A couple of pictures, perhaps, and some antique furniture. . . She hurried through to the hall to dial John Simpson's number.

She could tell from his voice that she'd woken him up, but after a few brief words from her he was wide awake, and in full control of the situation.

'You stay where you are!' he ordered firmly. 'I'll be over there as quick as I can.'

But no sooner had Helen put the receiver back on its cradle than she was upstairs again and pulling on jeans and a sweater.

She had no intention of staying where she was! It would take John Simpson at least ten minutes to get over here, and by that time whoever it was could have completely disappeared. And if it was burglars, who knew what they might do to the old house when they found there was nothing worth their attention?

She shivered and raced downstairs again to rummage in the hall cupboard for the flashlight, and the next moment, Rags at her heels, she was hurrying out across the lawn to the stream, and into the woods.

It was pitch-black among the trees, but she had the beam of the flashlight to guide her and she could hear Rags behind her, and after a couple of minutes' walking she was through the trees and staring out over the pastureland that stretched away in front of the Folly.

She didn't need the flashlight now and she switched it off. The moon had emerged from behind a cloud and the front of the house was bathed in silvery light. It all looked peacefully serene. There were no cars, no dark shapes creeping stealthily past the windows, and Helen turned to make her way round to the side of the house, keeping in the shadow of the trees all the while.

Through the hole in the barbed-wire fence and she was at the edge of the drive. A quick word to Rags to 'Heel, boy!' and she had melted into the shadow of the house itself.

The courtyard at the back of the house, with its attendant outbuildings, was darkly silent, and Helen listened for a moment before flicking the flashlight on again to swing it round in an arc of light. But there was nothing. All was still and quiet. Nothing unusual at all. And suddenly the tension that had kept her tautly alert and watchful began to drain away.

She'd been mistaken. There had been no car, and the light she'd seen had probably been a reflection.

She'd imagined it all.

Shoulders sagging, and wondering what on earth she was going to say to John Simpson when he arrived, she began to walk back towards the drive. She reached the corner of the house and swung the beam of the flashlight round in one last arc.

And then she saw the car.

It was long and low and black, parked right under the high hedge at the other side of the drive. No wonder she hadn't seen it! She flicked the flashlight off and backed up until she felt the solid house wall against her back.

And it was then she realised just how alone she was. Rags had completely disappeared!

'Rags!' she whispered fiercely, but there was no response, and now she began to feel the first real stirrings of fear. After all, the nearest house was Hall Farm, over a mile away—and what on earth was keeping John Simpson? It seemed an age since she had phoned him from the safety of the Lodge. . .!

Then she began to pull herself together. At least I have one advantage, she thought to herself. I know this place better than they do! And slowly she turned and began to creep stealthily back along the wall of the house, past the kitchen door, which was still firmly locked, towards the kitchen window.

Just beyond this was a small pantry window. It was the only window on the ground floor with a faulty catch, and within seconds Helen was puffing and grunting as she hauled herself through it into the gloom of the pantry.

Inside, the house was eerily silent, but it wasn't the silence that bothered her. What did bother her was the thought that there were intruders here, possibly already inside the house itself, and the thought of them running greedy fingers over Uncle Gerald's things, disturbing the serene tranquility of this place, filled her with a fierce anger, and as silently as she could she let herself out of the pantry and tiptoed across the moonlit kitchen to the hall door.

She opened it a fraction, then it creaked, making her almost jump out of her skin. She was motionless, hardly daring to breathe, expecting any minute to have some huge black form jump out at her from the darkness, but all she could hear was the pounding of her own heart, and after a moment she eased the door open a little further and squeezed through into the hall.

I'd better check the front door, she thought, and was already halfway across the tiled floor, almost at the foot of the stairs, when suddenly the chandelier above her head burst into brilliant life and she was blinded, petrified, falling back against the stairs with the flashlight flung in front of her ready to ward off any attack. But the attack, when it came, was a masculine voice, very deep and harsh, that seemed to reverberate round the panelled hall and into her stunned senses, making her body go rigid with shock and disbelief.

'Hello, Helen.'

Slowly, almost incredulously, she brought her head up and blinked dazedly across to where he still stood with his hand on the light switch, tall and broad and muscular-looking, with the same dark hair curling over the collar of a dark overcoat, and it was as though she was looking at a ghost.

But then he moved. His hand fell from the switch and was thrust into his pocket as he advanced into the hall, and the spell that had held her transfixed was shattered as his approach galvanised her into action. He stopped, eyes narrowing, as she desperately tried to pull herself together enough to stand up and face him, steadying herself with one hand on the banister.

Then she got out in a strained voice, 'Hello, Martyn.'

CHAPTER TWO

MARTYN'S eyes were still narrowed, piercingly intent, and they seemed to glitter strangely in the light from the chandelier. 'Good lord, Helen, you're the last person I expected to see——'

'Why are you here?' she interrupted unsteadily.

He seemed to hesitate for a moment, then his eyebrows rose, making him appear coolly aloof. 'I could ask you the same question.'

'I heard a car,' she managed to say. 'I thought you were a——'

'A burglar?' he finished for her. 'I'd already gathered that! What were you hoping to do—raid the place all on your own?' And the strange harshness in his voice, the old taunting hint of mockery, brought her back to her senses. Reaction was setting in now, dispelling the shock and that sudden, painful stab of cold fear and replacing them with a slow, burning anger that was beginning to uncurl from somewhere deep inside her.

'What can you expect when you insist on being so secretive?' she returned, her voice degrees colder now. 'After all, it is almost three o'clock in the morning! You could at least have informed someone you were coming—even if it was only Mr Winstanley——'

'The solicitor?' he interrupted harshly. 'I didn't even know the old boy was still alive, let alone working! Anyhow, he's the last person I'd report my movements to,' he continued bitingly. 'I need a break—nothing but peace and tranquillity! At the moment no one

even knows I've left London, and that's the way I
intend things to stay!'

'But—don't you know you can't stay here?' Helen
began, frowning now, and his eyebrows rose again.

'Why not?'

'Well, for one thing the house has been empty for
weeks. There are no rooms prepared—no bed——'

'That's never been a problem before.'

Something in his voice had her eyes jerking back to
his face, and a quiver ran through her as she met his
look. His eyes seemed to narrow even further as he
watched a tide of colour sweep from the base of her
throat and up over her cheeks, colour that, annoyingly,
she had no control over. But her inner emotions were
something else.

'The house is empty, Martyn,' she told him chillingly. 'There's nothing for you here now.'

'On the contrary, I've already discovered more than
I bargained for!'

'Uncle Gerald is dead!' she retorted, voice rising in
spite of her efforts to the contrary, and now his eyes
were two dark pinpricks of light as he watched her.

'You still use your childhood name for him,' he
declared softly. 'It always used to make me think we
were related in some way, Helen. That there was a
bond between us——'

'There's nothing between us!' she snapped, then
stopped abruptly, checking herself, struggling to retain
the shreds of her composure under that unnerving
stare. 'Why have you come?' she repeated tautly.

There was silence for a moment as he watched her,
then his shoulders moved in a brief shrug.

'I wanted to see the house again,' he told her coolly.
'Shall we say—for old times' sake?'

'Then why didn't you come when Gerald was ill?'

she demanded fiercely. 'All that time—the family must have known that this would be his final illness, and yet no one came near—there wasn't even a letter! And you—*you* must have known that he——'

'I didn't even know he was ill until a week ago!' he bit out. 'Believe me, it was a hell of a shock to discover he'd already died!'

'But you must have known!' she retorted, stunned both by the information and the way in which it was ground out of him. 'Mr Winstanley——'

'Your precious Mr Winstanley didn't even have the grace to inform me my uncle was ill!' he declared bitterly. 'Good heavens, Helen, do you think I'm so insensitive that I wouldn't have come if I'd known?'

He turned away, running frustrated fingers through his dark hair, and she watched him, before answering tautly, 'After all this time, you could at least have written to enquire how he was——'

'And he could have written to tell me he was dying!' Martyn retorted harshly.

'You know he would never communicate with the family.'

'Oh, no?' he queried caustically. 'He expected us to contact him, but he wouldn't stir himself even to put pen to paper! Good lord, Helen, you're as bad as he was. You expect the family to back down all the way, when he wouldn't even give an inch, and look where it's got him—absolutely nowhere! He was nothing but a stubborn, irascible old fool!'

'How can you say that?' she exclaimed, shocked. 'After all he did for you! You know you were the only one of the family he ever cared about——'

'That kind of caring I can do without!'

'He gave you help when you needed it!' she flung back. 'Nine years ago——' She stopped abruptly,

biting her lip, hesitating. Suddenly she was on dangerous ground—and they both knew it. At the mention
of that time Martyn's head had come up, and even in
this light she could see the tightness round his mouth,
the dangerous glint in eyes that were once more
narrowed and penetrating.

'Oh, yes, Helen?' he began softly. 'And just what
did my uncle do for me nine years ago?'

'He—he supported you——'

'He gave Simon Ashley several hundred pounds to
elope with *you*!' Martyn interrupted savagely.

There was a silence. Helen stared at him. 'How did
you find out about that?' she demanded. She was
white-faced now, trembling, burning with that bitter,
furious anger that was like a searing pain inside her.

'Does it matter?'

'I suppose you'll tell me now that you expected me
to wait for *you*?' she got out.

'I certainly didn't expect you to jump into bed with
Simon the minute my back was turned!' he retorted
acidly.

'You never meant to come back, did you?' she
accused fiercely. 'I was nothing more than a summer
fling to you!'

His face blazed, and then he seemed to check
himself, as though he was struggling for control, and
after a moment his mouth twisted into the semblance
of a smile, a smile that in other circumstances would
have chilled her to the bone.

'Looking at you now, Helen, it's hard to believe
butter wouldn't melt in your mouth!' he ground out.
'You look no different from the girl you were nine
years ago. It's incredible to think of what a fool I made
of myself over you!'

'And I was a fool to believe everything you told me,'

Helen flung back unsteadily. 'I should have remembered your name is *Sayton*!'

The smile faded. 'I should be careful if I were you, Helen. As you say, it's nearly three o'clock in the morning—and you still haven't given me a satisfactory explanation as to why you're creeping across my hall in the middle of the night!'

'*Your* hall?' she echoed, suddenly still. 'Don't you think you're being a little—*presumptuous*, Martyn? After all, your relationship with your father was never very——'

'My father has nothing to do with this!' he declared. 'And neither has presumption. When I say my hall, that's exactly what I mean!'

Once again she stared at him. 'I—I don't understand——'

'It's perfectly simple.' That crooked smile was back in place, and now she could feel its coldness shivering down her spine. 'Gerald Sayton did one thing for me, whether he meant to or not. He left me Sayton's Folly!'

Helen was silenced, staring at him uncomprehendingly. 'But—but he can't have done!' she got out at last. 'There was no will——'

'A will isn't necessary,' he retorted chillingly. 'I happen to be Gerald's next of kin!'

'But—but your father,' she stammered. 'He's Gerald's brother—and you have a brother——'

'Correction—had,' he told her, and his face was as clipped and hard as his words. 'When I said my father has nothing to do with this, that's just what I meant. You remember nine years ago—when I had to return to London to my brother's hospital bed?' She nodded dumbly, and he continued abruptly, 'He died. My

father never got over it. He had a heart attack and
died a couple of years later.'

'My God!' Helen whispered, appalled. And then,
'Martyn, I'm sorry! Gerald never told us——'

'He was hardly likely to, was he?' Martyn interrupted scathingly. 'Considering he spent most of his
life trying to believe my side of the family didn't exist!
I sometimes think he only helped me occasionally to
spite my father!'

For a brief moment there was a bleak look in his
eyes, and Helen found herself gripping the banister
rail so hard it almost hurt, but then his eyes came back
to her face and he continued with a thin, icy smile, 'So
you see, if anyone is being—*presumptuous*, Helen, it's
you. Your mother may have been Gerald's housekeeper, but that long-standing relationship doesn't
give you the right to come creeping around my house
in the middle of the night! And now, as I've been
travelling for most of the night——' he paused to
glance at his watch '—I intend to get some sleep, and
I suggest you leave—by the front door this time!'

His dismissal was curtly sarcastic, and any softening
Helen might have felt towards him shrivelled and died
inside her. 'I don't know what you mean,' she retorted
coldly.

'I mean that I heard you puffing and grunting
through the pantry window—and if you're hoping to
make a habit of entering houses by that method then
you should get youself into better condition!' His eyes
moved over her as he spoke, seeming to take in every
detail of her slim length, and once again Helen felt
herself colouring. 'I happened to be in the kitchen at
the time,' he added, by way of explanation. 'Looking
for the fuse box, as it happens.' His eyes had come
back up to her face, narrowing once more on her pink

cheeks. And then he added in a different tone, 'Of course, if you'd rather stay and make my bed. . .?'

Fuming now with embarrassment and humiliation and something else she couldn't quite fathom, Helen had already opened her mouth to tell him exactly what she would do for him, when there was a thunderous banging on the front door.

With a cold, questioning glance in her direction, Martyn strode across to fling the heavy door open—to reveal John Simpson, the policeman, and behind him, Rags.

Rags spotted Helen at once and bounded straight in, tail waving in joyful greeting, and even John Simpson looked straight past Martyn to where Helen was now fondling the dog's ears.

'Are you all right, Mrs Ashley?'

But Martyn had also turned back to look at Helen, his expression completely different from the policeman's relieved countenance. 'Well, *Mrs Ashley*?' he demanded, and Helen couldn't stop her eyes sliding uncomfortably away from his, 'Did you call the police?' he demanded curtly.

'Mrs Ashley did just what she should have done,' John Simpson interposed in his broad Cheshire accent. 'She was suspicious, so she called me.'

'I'm surprised she didn't organise a full reception committee while she was at it!' Martyn retorted caustically, and John Simpson eyed him narrowly.

'Do you mind telling me who you are, sir?'

'Why, are you going to charge me with something?' Martyn challenged angrily.

'Just for the record, sir,' John Simpson answered smoothly. 'After all, you never know who's prowling about in the middle of the night, especially near empty houses——'

'Well, this house isn't empty now, is it?' Martyn retorted sarcastically. 'I'm here—and I can assure you I have every right to be!'

'It's all right, John,' Helen put in, as the policeman began to pull out his notebook. 'This is Martyn Sayton—the new owner of Sayton's Folly.'

'Is that so?' John Simpson looked at Martyn with new interest, but Martyn was glaring at Helen.

'I came up here for some peace and quiet!' he snapped. 'Not to have my presence broadcast from the rooftops!'

'Then you shouldn't have arrived in the middle of the night!' Helen retorted coldly. 'And anyway, John is very discreet——'

'From what I remember, people in Penford don't even know the meaning of the word!' Martyn bit out, but the policeman seemed completely unruffled.

'I understand, sir.' He grinned. 'And you won't be disturbed again. As everything seems to be in order here, I'll say goodnight.'

'Me too,' Helen added hastily, and grabbed Rags's collar. The vulnerability of her position was beginning to come home to her, and the look on Martyn's face was none too pleasant. He had already taken a couple of steps towards her, but she slid out of the door, so placing the policeman strategically between them.

'Goodnight, Mr Sayton,' she returned coolly, from behind John Simpson's burly frame. 'Sleep well,' she added with caustic sweetness, and ignoring the look on his face, and with Rags at her heels, she walked away into the darkness, and only she knew the effort it cost her not to run all the way back to the Lodge.

In the cold light of day Helen's overriding impulse was still to run—to pack her bags and get herself and Jamie out of the Lodge and away from Sayton's Folly as quickly as possible. But, she told herself hollowly, what would be the point of that? As yet, they had nowhere to run to, and anyway, why should she feel that it was *she* who had to run away? Hadn't she spent the last nine years believing it was Martyn who was in the wrong? Wasn't *he* the one who had betrayed *her*?

And the way he had talked about Simon—almost as though he hated him. . . She closed her eyes against the painful throbbing in her temples. It was perfectly clear to her now why she was being evicted from the Lodge.

She sighed as she opened her eyes again. She'd been awake for most of what was left of the night, pacing the bedroom, racking her brains trying to decide what was best to do, and reluctantly she had come to the decision that there was only one thing to do, and that was to sit tight. After all, she still had six weeks—and Martyn might only be here to view his inheritance, and then he would disappear back to London again. Hadn't he said something last night about needing a break? Hadn't he mentioned peace and tranquillity?

Her mouth twisted into the semblance of a smile. He would certainly get that at the Folly at the moment! No heating, no food in the cupboards, none of the beds made up. . .!

She smiled grimly as she stared through the french windows of the sitting-room, up through the trees towards the Folly, and wondered what kind of night he had spent, all alone in that cold, empty house, and she snuggled further into her own warm dressing-gown. She was curled comfortably on the sofa in front of the fire. It was still early, but she was already on her third cup of coffee, and, as she sipped at her cup, her smile widened as she remembered Martyn's face last night when he had opened the door to John Simpson. She had told him the truth when she'd said John was discreet, but in Penford things had a way of getting around. She, more than anyone, knew that. She had no idea why Martyn had arrived in the middle of the night, wanting no one to know he was here, but by lunchtime it would be all round the village that there was a Sayton back at Sayton's Folly—and not the one they had expected either! It was just like old times, they would say, having Martyn back at the Folly. . .

Her smile froze as her cup clattered into its saucer. No, it wasn't like old times! Those times were dead and gone along with Gerald—and Simon! She was a woman now; mature, independent, with a son to care for; a world away from that gauche eighteen-year-old who had spent that last summer in a blaze of delirious happiness because she had been in love. . .

She groaned as she set her cup and saucer down unsteadily on the coffee-table and leaned back against the sofa, putting a weary hand up to her aching forehead. She had thought all these tortuous emotions buried and forgotten! After all, up until yesterday she had hardly even allowed herself to think about the past, and now, suddenly, it was surrounding her, invading every waking moment. . .!

She raised her head again to stare bleakly into the fire. Now, looking back, she was astounded that she could have been so foolish, so guillible as to believe that that summer had meant anything more to Martyn than all the other summers he had spent at Sayton's Folly. She should have remembered he was a Sayton—one of the *London* Saytons! Hadn't Gerald always hated them—and with good reason? She had told

Jamie that Gerald and his brother had had a falling out, but there was far more to it than that!

One of her favourite bedtime stories as a little girl had been the story of how Gerald, as a young man, had gone away to London and returned with a beautiful young bride, Lady Mary Ashbourne. Sarah herself had only been a young girl at the time, but she had seen the couple's return from London at first hand.

'She was exquisite,' she had used to tell Helen wistfully. 'Everyone who saw her loved her.'

Unfortunately that 'everyone' had also included Gerald's own younger brother, and it was only a few short months later that Lady Mary had left again, this time at dead of night, accompanied by Richard—her lover! The divorce case that had followed had rocked London society, with Lady Mary claiming mental cruelty, among other things, as one of her reasons for running away, with the accusation that Gerald had kept her locked up at Sayton's Folly, refusing to allow her access to the London friends and amusements she had been used to. Richard Sayton had managed to persuade Lady Mary's family and some of his own London relations to support them, and Gerald, broken and embittered, had shut himself away at Sayton's Folly, effectively cutting himself off from the world.

Tragically, just after the birth of her second son, Lady Mary had been killed in a road accident, running away, it had been said, from her second husband, who, ironically, had turned out to be just as much of a tyrant as she had claimed her first husband to be! But this, of course, had never been proved, and it had only served to compound Gerald's hatred of his brother and the rest of his family.

Only Martyn, as the rebellious younger son, had aroused any kind of empathy in Gerald. Whether,

because of Richard Sayton's treatment of Martyn
because of the association with his wife's death, Gerald
had actually felt sorry for Martyn, or whether, as
Martyn himself had so succinctly put it last night, he
had simply been using him to get back at his brother,
only Gerald had known, but for her, Martyn's holidays
from boarding-school, spent at Sayton's Folly, had
been an accepted part of childhood, and in her innocence she had never dreamed that one day she, too,
would play her part in that childhood fairy-tale.
Martyn had been accepted into her already established
friendship with Simon, and the two older boys had
simply been the brothers she had never had.

She gave a mirthless smile. Those childhood days
seemed like another lifetime now. The simple affec-
tions of childhood had given way to far more potent
emotions, and the childhood fairy-tale had taken on
an incredible reality the summer that Martyn had
returned from his final year at university, and suddenly
it had been as lovers that she'd found herself considering her two childhood playmates. Simon had always
been the quieter, more withdrawn of the two, and he
had always been her confidante, her best friend; but
Martyn had been stronger, both in physique and
personality, already possessing a male sophistication
the more gentle Simon could never have hoped to
achieve. Martyn had swept her off her feet with a
devastating completeness, and the fairy-tale had finally
shattered.

Once more Helen's mouth twisted mirthlessly. She
could look back on it all now with a certain amount of
detached cynicism; after all, she was no tragic Lady
Mary. She had survived—hadn't she? She was a living,
breathing woman with a son to care for, and in some
respects it was Jamie who had pulled her through. She

had even managed to complete her own university course, and now she was teaching, with the luck to get a job at Kingsleigh High. And she was back at Sayton's Folly. And if Martyn thought he could treat her now the way he had treated her nine years ago. . .!

But no, why should he? After all, if she had changed, then so had he—it had only taken one glance last night to tell her that. Nine years ago he had been on the brink of a career in art—something he had always desperately wanted and had been supremely capable of—despite his father's insistence that he should go into the family firm, and she had assumed that, whatever he had done, he had made a success of it; that overcoat hadn't been bought in any chain store, and, from what she'd seen, the dark business suit underneath it wasn't off-the-peg either! But there were other, more subtle and disturbing changes too. His hair was still as dark as it had ever been, and those grey eyes were still as penetrating, but they seemed colder, harder—and there were harsh lines from nose to jaw that gave him an air of cynical detachment which she found vaguely unsettling.

And the way he had talked about his father and his brother—was it something to do with their deaths that had carved those lines into his face? Or something else. Something, perhaps, to do with—Jacqueline?

Once more Helen looked out of the window, through the trees towards the Folly, and now her fingers were twisted tortuously in her lap, the knuckles showing white, but she was oblivious of the pain.

All these years—and the one person she had never been able to bring herself to think about was Jacqueline! But now the floodgates of memory were opened and it was too late to stop her mind being dragged painfully back to that bleak October day when

Simon had driven her down to London. Her mouth twisted bitterly. She had been desperate to see Martyn. Instead, she had been confronted by the tall, imposing figure of Richard Sayton, and a slim, dark-haired, dark-eyed beauty, only slightly different from herself in age, but completely different in looks and sophistication. Helen brought her eyes back to the fire, staring into its burning depths. No wonder Martyn's father had looked askance at her—she must have seemed like a wild country girl to him in comparison, with her old rain-splattered tweed coat and haunted, desperate eyes! Even now she could see the look on his face, the way he had introduced the other girl as Jacqueline Beauford, Martyn's fiancée. . .

Abruptly Helen reached for her coffee-cup again and stood up to pad restlessly through to the kitchen.

She had been unable to stop herself wondering whether or not Martyn had actually married the other girl—not that it mattered to her now either way. After all, that was all in the past—and hadn't Martyn indicated last night that for him too the past was dead and gone as far as she was concerned?

And if he had married Jacqueline, then she was probably still in London, waiting for him, all the more reason for his stay here to be short—and as far as she was concerned, the shorter the better! Because the sooner he returned to London, the sooner Helen and Jamie would be left in peace to find somewhere else to live—and that should be her main priority now, she told herself firmly, not torturing herself with memories from the past!

But it soon became clear that Jamie didn't share her view. She'd only just brought him back from Hall Farm later in the morning when he went out and saw the car. He came racing back to tell her, and she realised belatedly that she would have to have a serious talk with him.

'It's a Porsche!' he informed her excitedly. 'They're very expensive, you know, and this one has a sun roof and the most terrific wheel trim you ever saw——'

'Jamie, you mustn't go near it!' Helen exclaimed, horrified that he had even been up to the Folly without telling her. After all, if he should see Martyn—if Martyn should see *him*——!

'But it's parked on Uncle Gerald's drive! Is there someone at the Folly? Have you asked them about us?'

'Yes, there's someone at the Folly,' she evaded briefly, 'but I haven't said anything about us—and I don't want you saying anything either! In fact I don't want you going anywhere near the Folly from now on—understand?'

'But, Mum——!'

'*Listen* to me, Jamie,' she commanded tautly, grasping his shoulders and turning him abruptly round to face her. 'You mustn't say anything about us or our affairs to anyone—especially not to the man up at the Folly! *Promise* me, Jamie?' She stared at him, commanding his co-operation. 'And while he's here I think it would be best if you kept away from the big house. Play in your den—in the garden—but stay near the Lodge!'

Jamie was staring at her uncertainly, obviously crestfallen and puzzled by her attitude. But he didn't understand, Helen realised agitatedly. How could he?

'Jamie,' she continued, struggling to inject a note of reasonableness into her tone, 'Uncle Gerald has gone now, and someone else is at the Folly—a stranger. We have no place up there now—and soon we'll have left here altogether!' She gave him a gentle shake before releasing her grip on his shoulders and sitting back. 'And anyway, I think the man up at the Folly wants to be left alone, so it would be better if you and Rags stay away from there—I don't want you getting into trouble!' she added carefully, still watching him. 'OK?'

He was silent for a moment, obviously thinking it over. 'OK,' he muttered reluctantly, and she managed a smile.

'Good boy,' she murmured, giving him a quick hug, then watched him as he wandered disconsolately out again.

He doesn't understand, she repeated to herself, but there was nothing she could do about that. She didn't want him going anywhere near Martyn Sayton. Martyn was a part of the past—*her* past, and she had no intention of letting him anywhere near her son.

Helen stood on the patio, frowning out across the lawn. Jamie had muttered something about playing in his den, but that had been just after lunch, and it was now nearly teatime and she hadn't seen sight nor sound of him for at least an hour, she realised, as she glanced impatiently at her watch.

But then, lunch had been an unusually fraught affair, she thought with guilty irritation, and it had partly been her fault; but Jamie had spent the whole meal talking about 'the man up at the Folly'! So much so that it had completely turned her off her lunch— and Jamie had even managed to turn that into an inquisition! He'd surveyed the untouched left-overs and enquired casually—far too casually—why she didn't take some up to the man at the Folly.

'Nana always used to take Uncle Gerald his meals,' he had added innocently.

'That was different!' Helen had snapped. She had

no intention of doing for Martyn what her mother had done for Uncle Gerald. Besides, Martyn was perfectly capable of looking after himself! He had always known where his own best interests lay, she thought bitterly.

Of course, she could see what Jamie was trying to do. He was determined that she should ask Martyn about their staying on at the Lodge, but she would just have to make him see that this wasn't possible. There was no way now she was going to stay here with Martyn up at the Folly—and with another hiss of impatience she glared at her watch again and set off across the lawn to the shadow of the trees, calling experimentally, 'Jamie?'

There was no reply. Even Rags seemed to have disappeared, and she stood by the stream, staring uneasily into the trees. Surely he wouldn't deliberately disobey her—and certainly not so soon after being told?

'Jamie?' she called again. Still there was no reply, and now she began to feel the first real pangs of alarm. Surely he hadn't gone up to the Folly? Not after he'd specifically been told not to!

She crossed the stream and began to walk through the trees, searching the sunlit woods and calling all the while, but when there was still no reply she quickened her pace until she was almost running along the path. Really worried now, she scrambled through the barbed-wire fence and stood in the middle of the drive, staring at the huge mass of the house. 'Jamie!' she shouted again, and now alarm and anger at being disobeyed made her voice sound furiously shrill. She turned to march round to the courtyard at the back of the house, but as she rounded the corner the sight that met her eyes stopped her dead in her tracks.

Martyn stood in the middle of the courtyard,

unshaven, hair ruffled, and clad only in a very loosely tied towelling robe, and in that first split second Helen realised with a shock that he'd lost none of his magnetic masculinity—but almost immediately this thought was swept aside as she realised he wasn't alone. Jamie was with him, being grasped unceremoniously by the scruff of the neck, and suddenly anger and shock had turned to cold, hard fear.

'*Jamie!*' she cried, and at the sound of her voice they both turned.

'Do you know this boy?' Martyn demanded, and Helen hurried forward.

'Of course——'

'I caught him trying to let down the tyres of my car!' Martyn interrupted furiously, and once again Helen was stopped in her tracks.

'*What?*'

Shock and disbelief held her rigid. Rags was leaping about excitedly and barking, and almost without taking her eyes off Martyn and her son, she ordered abruptly. '*Quiet*, Rags!' To her relief, he immediately obeyed, and in those few brief seconds she managed to pull herself together.

'Perhaps you'd better tell me what happened?' she demanded unsteadily.

'He was caught in the act!' Martyn declared furiously. 'I looked out of the window and there he was—kneeling by the car!'

'But I was only looking!' Jamie wailed, finally giving way to his tears.

'*Looking?*' Martyn was obviously about to explode, but Helen was far more in control of herself now. The initial shock of seeing these two together was wearing off, and relief was flooding through her, relief that the situation was not as she had at first feared—but it was a relief mixed with anger. Anger at the way Martyn was treating Jamie, the way he was manhandling him. . .!

'Have you checked your tyre pressures?' she demanded to know, and Martyn's eyes flashed to her face, before darkening ominously.

'I don't believe this!' he ground out. 'Are you calling me a liar, Helen?'

Helen's eyebrows rose, haughtily aloof, a biting retort on the tip of her tongue, but she bit it back. 'Look around you, Martyn. This isn't exactly the backstreets of London!'

'I'm well aware of that!' he snapped.

'Then you must also be aware that in an area such as this a car like this is bound to attract attention,' she derided. 'I'm merely suggesting that you could be mistaking Jamie's motives——'

'I know what I saw!'

'You saw a boy kneeling by your car!' Helen countered as temper and other emotions she didn't care to analyse overcame everything else. 'An eight-year-old boy, Martyn. Look at him—there's more chance of me jumping over the moon than of a boy Jamie's size letting down the tyres on that car!'

'I can assure you, it's perfectly possible!'

'And I can assure you that Jamie would never dream of doing such a thing!'

'I've had enough of this,' Martyn muttered ominously. 'I don't give a damn for your assurances, Helen. I'm going to see the boy's father!'

'You'll have a job!' she retorted furiously. 'His father is dead!'

'Then I'll see his mother!' Martyn ground out, face implacable. 'Where does he live?'

'At the Lodge—with me,' Helen declared thunderously. 'Jamie is my son!'

There was a sudden silence, and now it was Martyn's turn to be stopped in his tracks. Her words had shocked him, Helen could see that, and at first she thought he was going to say he didn't believe her. He stared at her, and then at Jamie, and the shock obviously affected his reflexes, for his grip on the boy slackened and Jamie came running to her.

'You can be sure Jamie won't bother you again,' Helen informed him with chilling hauteur, 'and neither will I! And, of course, if there is any damage to the car, it will be paid for—although if you find so much as a finger-mark on it I'll be very much surprised!' she derided icily. 'However, if our paths should happen to cross in the next few weeks, I'll thank you not to manhandle my son unless you have my express permission!' And with that she called to Rags and turned and marched away, towing a still sniffing Jamie behind her, and Martyn was left standing in the cobbled yard, staring after them.

What a beast! Helen fumed, as she marched down the drive. He hadn't changed in that respect—he still had the Sayton temper! Well, he was welcome to it—he was welcome to the house and the Lodge too. For all she cared now, the whole damn lot could be razed to the ground—preferably with him in it!

CHAPTER THREE

AFTER the weekend, school on Monday morning seemed like a haven of normality. The usual bustle and noise for once had a relatively calming effect, and Helen even found herself smiling a little as she gave David Evans a brief account of her weekend as they sat in the staff-room at lunchtime.

But David didn't smile. He was watching her face, noting the tightness round her mouth, the way her fingers fiddled constantly with the spoon in her saucer. They were both having a much-needed cup of tea.

'This Martyn Sayton sounds a bit of a swine,' he said now. 'You want to be careful, Helen. Even though you've been asked to leave, as a tenant you still have rights. Don't let him push you around.'

'Don't worry, David, we aim to see as little of him as possible,' Helen returned with a tight little smile. David didn't know the half of it! 'Anyway, we can take care of ourselves.'

'Hmm, I'm not so sure. . .' David frowned. 'If he's as old and crotchety as Gerald was——'

'He may be crotchety, David, but he certainly isn't old!' Helen interrupted, smiling in spite of herself at this picture of Martyn, and David looked surprised.

'I thought you said he was?'

'Did I?' Helen raised her eyebrows.

'You said he was a relation of Gerald's.' David pointed out, 'and naturally I assumed. . .' He left the sentence unfinished, but his face wore an air of frowning persistence as his eyes met hers, and Helen sighed.

She'd known David ever since she'd first started teaching at Kingsleigh, and though their friendship now extended to well beyond school hours, it was strictly platonic, and she was quite happy to keep it that way—even though she knew David would leap at the chance to take it further. But she had no wish for complications of that sort, not with David, and anyway, she had Jamie to consider.

'He's Gerald's nephew,' she supplied now, as David continued his penetrating stare. 'I knew him years ago—when I was younger,' she added tonelessly. 'Of course, he's changed a lot since then——'

'How well did you know him?' David demanded to know, and Helen picked up her cup with careful fingers.

'He used to come down from London to stay with Gerald.'

'In that case, there's even more reason for you to be careful!' David told her, his frown intensifying. 'You know what these city folk are like—and this one has money to boot, by the sound of it! He probably still thinks he has the "droit de seigneur" or something——'

Helen nearly choked on her tea. 'David, you make it sound positively medieval!' she exclaimed, trying not to laugh. 'Anyway, Martyn isn't like that——'

She stopped, the laughter catching painfully in her throat. Martyn *was* like that! Didn't that phrase sum up their relationship in a nutshell? Once upon a time she had thought she knew him, but all that had changed nine years ago—and now he was even going to the extreme of evicting them from the Lodge!

But David was continuing gruffly. 'Well, you are alone there, Helen, and I don't want to frighten you, but——'

'But this is the twentieth century, David,' Helen interrupted impatiently, 'and I'm not exactly an innocent young maiden! I have Jamie, remember? And the dog.'

'They're hardly a protection, Helen!'

'They're protection enough,' Helen retorted, her voice cold now. 'Especially with a man like Martyn Sayton! They represent things like responsibility, David, and commitment. Things that Martyn Sayton doesn't understand and has no time for! All he understands is now—the present—and what he can get out of it——' She stopped abruptly, clamping her teeth together. Even to her own ears her voice sounded increasingly brittle and hard-edged, but David seemed hardly to be listening. He was glancing round the empty staff-room, as though checking that there was no one to overhear, then he leaned forward, his face earnestly serious.

'There is one way out of this,' he said. 'A way that would solve all your problems, financial and otherwise, at a stroke.'

Helen was staring into her tea, still struggling to get a grip on forgotten emotions that persisted in surging back and surprising her. 'Oh, yes?'

'Yes.' David was silent for a moment, then he said quietly, 'Marry me, Helen.'

Helen looked up then. 'Oh, David——!' she began, suddenly unsure if he was joking or not, but one look at his face told her he wasn't, and the words died in her throat.

'Listen to me for a moment, Helen, please,' he continued earnestly. 'You need a place to live—well, I have a house. You can move in with me. It's not exactly big, as you know, but it's big enough—and there's a garden. You could even bring that scruffy mongrel of yours——'

'David—*please*!'

The tone of her voice silenced him, but then Helen was silent too, biting her lip as she hesitated, searching for the right words.

'David, that's very sweet of you, but. . .' She hesitated again, and David stared at her for a moment, as though he could read in her face what she was trying to say, then he slumped back in his chair, expelling his breath in a harsh sigh.

'Don't tell me,' he said wearily. 'Your heart already belongs to another.'

She nodded, silent.

'Jamie,' he said flatly. And then, almost impatiently, 'When will you realise, Helen, that that boy of yours won't always need you? Perhaps then you'll realise just how much you've been missing out on all these years!'

'Why—because I won't marry you?' Helen quipped in an attempt at lightness.

'Of course not!' He was hurt now, she could tell, and trying not to show it. 'That's not what I meant at all—and you know it! You're a very attractive woman, Helen, if only you'd realise it——' He came to an abrupt halt as her hand covered his.

'David, you're very sweet, and I understand—really I do,' she told him gently. 'But you're a confirmed bachelor! You're happy as you are, and you know you can't stand the sight of children before nine o'clock in the morning.'

'Men have been known to change for less, Helen.'

Some men, perhaps, Helen thought hollowly. But some men simply reveal their true colours! But she didn't say anything to David. How could she? She knew he thought she had refused him because of Jamie, because she was still grieving for Simon—the husband she had lost. She had never been able to bring herself to tell him, to tell anyone, that in reality she had never been a *proper* wife at all.

Helen stared at Jamie in consternation. He had just accused her of lying to him, and she could hardly believe she had heard aright.

He had been very subdued all day—in fact, he had been subdued since the scene with Martyn yesterday, and she had assumed it was remorse for his part in the proceedings, but now it seemed she had assumed wrong.

'I think you'd better explain,' she said, her voice dangerously quiet.

'Why did you tell me the man up at the Folly was a stranger?' he burst out tremulously, and in the silence that followed she could only stare at him, shaken as much by his astuteness as anything else.

Then she told him slowly, 'He is a stranger, Jamie. At least, he is to you.'

'But you know him, don't you?' he accused. 'You called him by his name—and he knows you too!'

'I knew him a long time ago. Before you were born.'

'Was he a friend of Dad's?'

Now she had to sit down. Luckily the sofa was just behind her and she sank on to it, while Jamie stood over her, legs apart, hands on hips, almost as though he was interrogating her, and for the first time she was forced to acknowledge that perhaps there was more of Martyn in him than she had cared to admit. 'For a while—yes,' she answered.

'Then why is he making us leave here?' Jamie

demanded to know. 'Have you had a row with him or something?'

She stared up at her son, almost in exasperation now. 'Jamie, there are a lot of things you are too young to understand.'

'I'm not a baby, Mum!'

She half smiled. 'I'm beginning to realise that!' she murmured, half to herself. 'But what happened was a long time ago, Jamie, and it probably has nothing to do with our leaving the Lodge——'

She stopped, biting her lip. That was probably a lie, and Jamie was the one person she didn't want to have to lie to. She could hold David at arm's length with no problem, she could even face up to Martyn, but Jamie was something else. . .

'The Folly needs a lot of repairs——' she continued abruptly.

'I know that!' Jamie interrupted irritably.

'Then why won't you believe what I tell you?' she reasoned. 'I told you to keep away from Martyn Sayton, and you can see why now, can't you? He has the devil's own temper! If he sees you again he'll probably give you a good hiding—which is what you deserve if you go up to the Folly again without telling me!'

'But, Mum——!'

'No more questions!' she declared firmly, and stood up, effectively cutting off what he had been about to say. 'It's late and I'm tired,' which was perfectly true. Since Martyn's arrival she seemed to have been in a state of constant mental turmoil! 'Off to bed with you!' she ordered, and packed him off upstairs, so ending what for her had been a difficult few minutes, and it could only get harder, she realised with a pang. Jamie was growing up fast, and he was beginning to display a lot of his father's singlemindedness. She would have to be very careful—especially while Martyn was up at the Folly, she realised. Otherwise there might come a time when she could no longer hide the truth—from either of them!

Sayton's Folly had been very quiet, only the black Porsche still parked on the drive giving any evidence of Martyn's presence, and she had begun to think that after the scene with the car he had decided to leave them alone after all. But she was doomed to disappointment. The very next evening, as she was out in the garden making an effort to weed her mother's rose border, she caught sight of Martyn's tall figure striding determinedly down the drive. She glanced across at Jamie, who was finishing off his homework on the patio, and from the look he gave her she knew he'd seen him too. Jamie bent his head to his homework, and she bent back to the weeding, but not for long.

He's coming here! she realised in sudden apprehension, and sure enough Martyn headed straight for the little garden gate and through it to where she was working at the edge of the lawn. She had been kneeling on the grass, but now she straightened to meet him, stiffening as his eyes moved over her faded jeans and brief summer top. It was an effort to speak.

'Yes?' she enquired coldly, dreading what was to come.

A muscle jerked in his cheek, and he looked across to where Jamie was still bending studiously over his homework.

'Why didn't you tell me?' he said at last, and when she stared at him uncomprehendingly, he continued 'About Simon. About the boy.'

She was still clutching the garden fork, but now she half turned away from him to stick it upright into the lawn while she slowly began to take off the tattered old gloves she used for gardening.

'I thought you knew,' she declared flatly, and heard his hiss of frustration as the breath exploded from between his teeth.

'For heaven's sake, Helen, how could I know if you didn't tell me?' he erupted, but she was unmoved.

'Gerald knew.'

'He certainly wouldn't tell me!' he declared. 'Anyhow, I've been abroad for most of the last few years. The last I heard you'd only just married——'

'Well, now you know I have a son,' she returned coolly, and his eyes came back to hers.

'When did Simon——?' he began, and this time she didn't pretend to misunderstand him.

'Jamie was about eighteen months old when Simon died,' she answered. 'But he'd been ill for a long time before that.'

'And you've been alone since then?' he questioned abruptly. 'There's been no one else?'

She faced him angrily. 'Despite what you seem to think, Martyn, I don't go around looking for affairs with men! And even if I had the inclination, which I haven't, I certainly wouldn't have the time. I've spent the last eight years bringing up my son!'

She turned as she felt Jamie beside her, and put her arm across his young shoulders. He leaned protectively against her, hands in his pockets, his face set in lines of aggressive disapproval. It was the stance he always adopted with David, but this time Helen felt no exasperation. He had every reason to dislike Martyn.

Martyn, too, was staring at Jamie. 'I should have realised, Helen,' he murmured. 'He's exactly like you. The same hair, the same eyes. . .'

He squatted down in front of him. 'Tell me, Jamie,' he began, 'do you remember your dad?'

'No,' Jamie muttered. 'He died when I was small.' And then, to Helen's surprise, 'Mum told me you knew him.'

'Yes, I did.' Martyn's glance flicked to Helen for a moment. 'When we were your age we all used to play together—me, your dad and your mum.'

'Really?' Jamie was obviously interested now, and trying not to show it.

'Did your mum tell you why we all fell out?'

'No.' Jamie shook his head, wide-eyed now with curiosity. 'All she said was that it was a long time ago.' And Martyn smiled a wry, crooked little smile.

'Your mum said she was going to marry me, but she married your dad instead.'

'Really?' Jamie said again, and looked at Helen now as though he'd never seen her before. 'She said I was too young to understand,' he said to Martyn, and Helen could only stand there, twisted up inside with anger, frustration, fear. . .But there was nothing she could do, or say. Not in front of Jamie. And Martyn knew it! She glared at him, her hand clenched now where it still lay on Jamie's shoulder.

So that was how his mind was working, was it? she thought furiously. Using her son, an eight-year-old child, as a pawn in his game against her?

Martyn was still smiling that same crooked smile. 'I could have been your dad,' he said to Jamie now. Helen went rigid, but Jamie was staring thoughtfully at Martyn.

'I'm not sure I'd like that,' he said at last. 'You've got a bad temper—even Mum says that.'

Now Martyn was really smiling. 'Your mum's right.' He stood up slowly, without taking his eyes off Jamie's face. 'I shouldn't have let fly at you the other day when I caught you looking at my car—but from where I stood at the window it looked like something else.'

Jamie was still looking thoughtful. 'No, it was my fault,' he said, and now Helen was staring at him in astonishment. 'Mum had already told me to keep away.'

'You and me—we've got off to a bad start,' Martyn told him. 'Perhaps we should start over—try again. What do you think?'

'I'd like that,' Jamie answered, and then, in a very adult fashion, he held out his hand, and Martyn took it. 'Perhaps—if you don't mind, that is—I could arrange a convenient time to have a look at the car properly?' Jamie asked, and Martyn nodded solemnly.

'Of course. We'll arrange it between us.'

And for the first time, Jamie smiled. 'I have to finish my homework now,' he said apologetically, and with a quick glance at Helen he turned and walked slowly back to where his books were still sprawled out on the patio, while Helen watched him gathering them up, hardly able to believe what she had just heard.

She turned furiously back to Martyn. In a few brief minutes he had won Jamie over completely, using nothing but Jamie's insatiable curiosity about Simon. But it was all a pretence—it had to be! There could be no reason for it other than Martyn's determination to get back at her—and he was certainly succeeding in that! For Jamie it could end in nothing but tears, and it was that that made her so angry.

'Martyn——!' she began furiously, but he forestalled her, his eyes still on Jamie's disappearing figure.

'He's an intelligent kid,' he commented. 'You've done a good job with him, Helen.'

Helen's face felt frozen. 'I want you to keep away

from him,' she got out, and Martyn turned to her now, eyebrows raised.

'He's just a child,' she muttered tautly. 'He has nothing to do with anything—certainly not with anything that happened years ago! I won't have you using him.'

'You really do think I'm an insensitive bastard, don't you, Helen?' he enquired in a voice that was suddenly harshly brittle, and Helen looked away from him to stare fixedly at a point somewhere over his shoulder.

'We'll be leaving here soon,' she continued, in that same taut tone. 'And we'll probably never see you again.'

'You sound very sure of that!'

'I don't want Jamie getting hurt!'

He was silent for a moment, staring at her, then he asked caustically, 'I take it you have no objections if I take him for a ride in the Porsche?'

Yes, she did have objections! But she couldn't very well voice them. 'He'll love that,' she got out through stiff lips.

'In that case, I'll arrange to take him one night after school,' he told her harshly. 'And now that I've made my peace with Jamie, I'll get on to my other main reason for coming down here, which was to see Sarah. Is she about?'

Helen's eyes had jerked back to his face in disbelief. 'You want to see—my mother?' she gasped.

'She must have had a hard time with Gerald at the end,' he said. 'I want to give her my thanks, and ask her if she'll continue as housekeeper at the Folly while I'm here. Of course it will be nothing on the scale of what she did for Gerald,' he continued. 'Just cooking and the odd bit of cleaning. I'm very easy to look after,' he added, and his eyes were full of mockery as they met hers, but then he registered the shock on her face, and suddenly he was frowning. 'Despite what happened between *us*, Helen,' he bit out, 'I thought Sarah would be happy to continue at the Folly.'

'Are you trying to tell me you don't know?' she questioned abruptly, but she already knew the answer to that. She could tell from his face that he hadn't a clue what she was talking about, and unless he was a brilliant actor there was no way he could hide it to that extent. . .

'My mother is dead,' she declared through stiff lips, and watched his face as her words had their effect. His features changed, his pupils dilated with shock.

No, he hadn't known.

But why hadn't he known? she asked herself in bewilderment. He was the new owner of Sayton's Folly. He was the one who was evicting them—and she knew Mr Winstanley had sent all the details——

'What happened?' Martyn demanded to know. 'Was she ill?'

'Only for a couple of days,' Helen told him, still struggling to make sense of what she had just discovered. 'None of us expected it—least of all my mother. It was a terrible shock.'

'When did it happen?'

'A couple of days after your uncle.' She paused. She would have to tell him about Sarah. It was the least she could do. 'I thought it was reaction after Gerald's death at first,' she explained. 'But the doctor rushed her into hospital for tests—and the next thing I knew——' She swallowed painfully.

'And you've been alone here ever since?'

She nodded. 'Mr Winstanley has been marvellous. When we didn't hear anything from London, from the family, he helped me with all the arrangements—and then he wrote to London again for me.'

'It must have been hell for you,' Martyn murmured, almost to himself. He was staring at the house, at the garden. Sarah's garden. 'I was very fond of her. When I came here as a kid she was like a mother to me—but then you know that.'

Helen stared at him dumbly as memories of those far-off summers came surging back, and then suddenly tears were pricking at her eyelids and she was struggling to control a flood of emotion.

'Good lord, no wonder you thought I was a burglar that night,' Martyn muttered harshly. 'You must have been scared out of your wits! And what in heaven's name possessed you to come up to the Folly in the middle of the night like that?'

His face had tautened and he was watching her now, his eyes narrowed and penetrating, almost accusing.

'I'd already called the police——' she got out, but he swore savagely.

'And if I'd been a real burglar—and inclined to violence?'

She stiffened. 'I don't need your concern——!' she began, but he was already continuing brutally.

'What would have happened to Jamie?'

She took a breath. Although at the time she had hardly considered the danger, she had certainly thought about it since! But there was no way she was going to admit that to Martyn. 'Jamie is my responsibility,' she declared unsteadily. 'And we can take care of ourselves.'

'A woman and child alone with a huge empty house, miles from anywhere?' he grated. 'It seems to me I arrived just in time!'

'On the contrary, you arrived nine years too late!'

she snapped. 'We don't need you here, Martyn. We don't want you in our lives. We can take care of ourselves!'

He stared at her, and the look in his eyes made her shiver.

'Yes, I do believe you can,' he grated. 'But then you always could, couldn't you, Helen? You've never needed anyone in your life! That cool beauty of yours may be devastating on the outside, but it hides a heart of stone!'

And with that he turned and slammed out of the gate and marched back up the drive to the Folly.

CHAPTER FOUR

THE weather had been fine and warm, but by the end of the week it had turned much cooler, and on Friday it rained steadily all day. It matched Helen's mood. For some reason she seemed to have had a deep depression over her ever since Martyn's parting words to her the other evening—and Jamie's permanent smile since his ride in the Porsche only seemed to make it worse. Martyn had come to pick him up, waiting in the car while Jamie had run out to him, and even when he'd dropped him off an hour later there hadn't been so much as a glance in her direction. Jamie, too, had seemed offhand with her, only telling her where they'd been when she'd questioned him about it—and all the time, at the back of her mind, there had been the question of why Martyn hadn't known about Sarah's death.

But she had other problems too.

She'd been to see the Head, to explain to him that she might not be able to return to Kingsleigh High after the summer. He had been very understanding about it, even to the extent of offering to arrange a transfer for her to another school, should she need it, but when David had found out he had been furious.

'Of course you'll be here in September! I've told you, Helen, my offer's still open; but if you still don't want to take me up on it then we'll find you somewhere to live in Kingsleigh——'

She had given a heavy sigh. 'David, you don't understand; I don't think I'll be able to afford a house in Kingsleigh—certainly not to buy!' she'd explained. 'And there's hardly any rented accommodation. After all, Kingsleigh is only a small market town.'

'Leave it to me,' he had declared firmly. 'I know one or two people in the property market. I'll ask around. Something's bound to turn up.'

Helen hadn't been so sure, but she'd nodded assent and given him a grateful smile which had immediately cheered him up, but it was beginning to occur to her that a complete break, both from Kingsleigh and from David, might be the best thing in the long run. His proposal had taken her completely by surprise. She had obviously seriously underestimated his feelings— but she had no intention of hurting him any more than was necessary.

Consequently, when she drove through the gates of the Folly that evening she had a thundering headache, as well as a pile of work for the weekend—but at least it *was* the weekend, she thought in relief. David was coming for dinner tomorrow, but until then——

'Mum, what's all that smoke up there?'

The abrupt sharpness of Jamie's question made her look round in surprise—to see a huge pall of black smoke hanging over the back of the Folly.

'Oh, no, *the Folly's on fire!*' she gasped, but even as she brought the car to an abrupt halt, Jamie was out of it and racing up towards the big house.

'Jamie, be careful!' she cried, but he ignored her, and with a muffled curse she slammed the car door and set off after him, breaking into a run as she hit the more level surface of the drive.

The smoke looked worse the closer she got, and suddenly fear was spurring her onwards. She rounded the corner of the house, gasping for breath now, to find the courtyard full of it. The kitchen door stood wide open, and it was here that the smoke was coming from, billowing forth in great, choking black clouds.

'*Jamie!*' Helen gasped, and without a second's hesitation stumbled forward into the kitchen.

She couldn't see anything for smoke at first, but then she made out Martyn's tall figure. He seemed to be jumping up and down on something on the floor, and Jamie was there too, beating at it with what looked like a brush, and suddenly Helen knew what had caused all this.

She raced out into the courtyard again to the outside tap. There was a garden hose connected to it, and, praying that it hadn't perished with years of neglect, she turned the tap on and grabbed the end of the hose to race back into the kitchen with it. The water spurted, then stopped, then spurted again, and there was an exclamation from the depths of the smoke. The flames hissed and died, but she continued to spray everything in sight, first the furniture, and then, finally, the ancient solid-fuel boiler in the corner.

At last, satisfied, she threw down the hose and went to turn the tap off again, before returning to survey what was left of the kitchen. It looked a mess. The walls and ceiling were blackened with smoke, and the tiles on the floor were swimming in water.

'*That damn boiler!*' Martyn exploded. 'Gerald should have replaced it years ago! I'd just got the bloody thing lit when it blew back at me—set the rug on fire and damn near half the kitchen as well!' He ran his fingers through his hair, then turned abruptly to glare at Helen. 'I don't know what you find so damn funny!' he bit out.

She was leaning against the door-jamb, giggling helplessly. It was the reaction, she supposed, but she couldn't help it. Now that the smoke had cleared

Martyn looked so funny! His hair stood on end, and he was covered from head to foot in black soot. He was dripping wet, too, from when she'd sprayed him with the hose, and every time he moved there was a funny sloshing sound.

'If you could see yourself——' she gasped, and collapsed into laughter again.

Jamie too was beginning to giggle, his small teeth very white against his black sooty face, but Martyn remained frozen, glaring at Helen. Then slowly his mouth began to twitch.

'I think it's a question of the pot calling the kettle black,' he drawled, and began to grin.

Helen straightened, her laughter fading. 'What do you mean?'

Martyn sloshed over to the far wall and took down the small mirror that usually hung there. He wiped some of the soot off it and held it out. 'Take a look,' he chuckled.

She stared at him, and then at her reflection. Her face too was dirty and smudged with black—it was even on her hair!

And then suddenly all three of them were helpless, holding their sides in uproarious laughter. . .

When, finally, they sobered, Martyn looked round the blackened kitchen. 'I'd better make a start on cleaning this place up,' he began, surveying the remains of the rug. 'And it looks as though I'm going to need some help. . .'

He looked at Helen, his eyes very direct, darkly grey, their message unmistakable, and a sudden warmth had Helen's breath catching in her throat; but then the feeling was gone, and her voice, when it came, sounded cool and remote.

'You'll catch a chill if you don't get out of those wet

things. What you need is a shower and a change of clothes.'

'I need some warmth!' he declared, and now his eyes were as cold as her voice had been. 'Why do you think I was trying to light the boiler?' His words had a double meaning which she couldn't help but be aware of, and she shifted uncomfortably; but now Martyn wasn't even looking at her. He was sloshing round the kitchen, inspecting the debris, throwing aside one of Gerald's old kitchen chairs that was now charred almost beyond recognition.

'Every time I need hot water I have to boil the kettle,' he continued, aiming his foot at what was left of the boiler. 'And now that the weather's changed this house seems to have more holes in it than a damn cheese grater! Lord knows what it's like in winter— how Gerald survived here as long as he did I'll never know!'

Helen opened her mouth to give him a crushing retort. After all, the house had been shut up for weeks—and hadn't she warned him how uncomfortable he would be? But Jamie got in first.

'We've got hot water,' he announced blithely, and Helen turned to stare at him, suddenly rigid, dreading what he was going to say next and yet helpless to prevent it. 'We haven't got a shower, but we've got a bath. Why don't you come to our house?'

And now all eyes were on Helen. Suddenly events were out of her control and moving much too fast, and she didn't like it.

'You could stay for tea,' Jamie said to Martyn, 'and then Mum will light the boiler for you. She knows how to do it, don't you, Mum?'

'Well, I——' Helen stammered, and stared from one to the other of them. Martyn was leaning against the boiler now, almost nonchalant, watching her through narrowed eyes while his mouth was twisted into a lop-sided grin. He had her in a corner, and he knew it. Jamie looked so expectant, so hopeful. . .

'Of course,' she said lamely at last. And then to Martyn, 'You're very welcome.' What else could she say? 'I'll go and get everything ready while you sort out a change of clothes and lock up here,' she muttered.

Jamie's whoop of glee covered up for any lack of enthusiasm on her part, but as she began to walk back down the drive towards the Lodge she felt her head-ache return in full force.

Jamie took charge of Martyn right from the start, and, to Helen's surprise, Martyn seemed to be enjoy-ing himself hugely. As soon as Rags had been let out and greeted, Jamie showed Martyn where the sitting-room was, where they ate their meals, where the bathroom was, and finally, where Martyn could change.

'Martyn has been here before, Jamie,' Helen told him testily. 'He knows his way around.' But Jamie refused to be put down.

'That was probably before I was born,' he pointed out reasonably. 'And besides, he doesn't know where the clean towels are.' And Helen returned to preparing their meal in tight-lipped silence.

She felt flustered and uncomfortable. The house was claustrophobic with Martyn in it, and she was reluctant to go upstairs and change as she usually did, knowing that he was there. Instead she took Sarah's old apron and tied it over the blouse and skirt she had worn for school. She could hear Martyn humming to himself in the bath, and, occasionally, Jamie's voice as he talked to him through the bathroom door. They're getting on

like a house on fire, she thought to herself, and
wondered why the knowledge should fill her with such
a feeling of guilty anxiety.

She remembered Sarah saying to her once, 'Jamie
needs a father, Helen. You can only give him so much;
when he gets older he'll need a man's hand.'

'What do you want me to do—go out and buy him
one?' Helen had quipped, but now, irrationally, she
found herself thinking that perhaps she had been
wrong all these years; that perhaps there was more she
could have done. . .

'Need any help?'

She swung round. Martyn stood just inside the
kitchen door, watching her, and even across the width
of the kitchen she could smell his cologne. It smelt
delicious, and he had changed into a fine wool jumper
and clean jeans.

'I—I think there's a bottle of wine in the cupboard,'
she got out. 'Could you see to it?'

He reached into the cupboard for the bottle, and
she turned back to the vegetables.

'Mmm. . . Not a bad label,' he remarked. 'I see you
know a thing or two about wine as well.'

Helen remained silent. The bottle was one David
had brought ages ago and they'd never got round to
opening, but she wasn't going to tell Martyn that!

He put it into the fridge, then she nearly jumped
out of her skin as she felt him right behind her, and his
voice came in her ear, 'Why don't you let me see to
those?'

Before she could react he had reached in front of
her and taken the vegetable knife out of her hand.
'It'll give the wine time to chill—and you time to
change into something more—relaxing.' His eyes
flicked smoothly over the blouse and skirt.

'Why don't you go and lay the table?' she retorted chillingly, but his smile never altered.

'Jamie's seeing to it,' he said, and she was left staring at him helplessly, noticing inconsequentially that his hair was still damp.

'There's still plenty of hot water,' he said, watching her. 'Why don't you go up and soak for a while? I can take care of things down here.'

I'll bet you can! Helen thought, but the words remained unsaid as she bit her lip with them still on the tip of her tongue. There was no malice in his face—nothing. He seemed to be making a genuine effort to be courteously polite—and she was being obstinately bitchy!

And it was only for a couple of hours, after all, she told herself hollowly. Perhaps she should just try and accept the situation—for Jamie's sake, if nothing else.

'Thanks,' she muttered reluctantly. And then, after a short silence, 'We're having peas as well. They're in the freezer.' And with that she threw down the apron and left him to it.

Upstairs, she flopped down in front of the dressing-table feeling absolutely drained. She looked it too, she realised, as she caught sight of herself in the mirror. No wonder Martyn had suggested she have a soak! Her face still had the odd smudge of black on it—and her hair looked a mess! Perhaps a bath wasn't such a bad idea after all. . .

Afterwards, brushing her newly washed hair in the mirror, she felt much better—and she looked much better too, she thought, surveying the blue velour leisure suit that exactly matched the colour of her eyes. On impulse, she added a touch of eye colour and some lip gloss, then hurried downstairs to the kitchen again, only to find it empty and everything apparently under control, and when she walked through to the sitting-room it was to find Martyn and Jamie side by side on the sofa, watching television.

'Mum, you look great!' Jamie exclaimed when he saw her, and Martyn too seemed to have a strange look on his face, but before he could speak Helen announced abruptly,

'Everything's ready. Shall we eat?' and went back to the kitchen to start serving up.

The meal went well, even Helen had to admit that. Perhaps it was the wine, she thought, and looked across at Martyn. He was laughing at something Jamie had said, and he too seemed relaxed and comfortable. He'd eaten a hearty meal, and Helen found herself wondering now if he'd had any proper meals at all since he'd been at the Folly. After all, she knew there was nothing edible up there, and he'd hardly been out—except when he'd taken Jamie for a ride in the Porsche.

Well, he's old enough to take care of himself! she thought acidly. And why should she worry whether or not he was eating properly? Just because he was getting on so well with Jamie——!

She brought her thoughts to an abrupt halt and finished her wine.

They had coffee in front of the fire. Jamie got out his Monopoly, but Helen had no intention of playing cosy family board games with Martyn and she stood up, with the excuse that the dishes needed doing; but Martyn stood up too, facing her over Jamie's head, his eyes dark in the firelight as he looked at her.

'Don't be a spoilsport, Helen,' he murmured, and something in his tone sent a prickle of awareness quivering along her senses. His voice seemed almost as deep and dark as his eyes. 'The dishes can wait. It'll make the game more—*interesting* if we all play.' And then, as she still hesitated, 'Don't you agree, Jamie?'

'Yes!' Jamie chimed in, his lighter tones almost as huskily persuasive as Martyn's had been. 'Come on, Mum. You can be the banker—then you can check if Martyn's cheating or not!'

If only I could! The words flashed into Helen's mind as she sank down to the sofa again, but she didn't voice her thoughts, and only the tightness round her mouth gave any sign of what she was feeling.

Despite her reluctance, Helen soon found herself enjoying the game, and by the time Jamie gleefully announced that he had won—with a little help from Martyn—she was surprised to discover how late it was.

'Come on, young man,' she said to Jamie. 'It's past your bedtime.'

'But Mum, it's Friday,' he pleaded. 'And you haven't lit Martyn's boiler yet.'

'No, and she isn't going to,' Martyn said, surprising them both. 'Not tonight, anyway. It's raining again— or hadn't you noticed? And anyway, I'm not even sure the boiler will light now after the dousing it got from the hosepipe earlier——'

'I hardly touched it with the hose!' Helen retorted. 'And anyway, I don't mind——'

'But I do!' Martyn said, suddenly silencing her. And then, in a gentler tone, he added, 'Believe me, Helen, I had a look at it before I came down here earlier, and I think it would be better if it was left to dry out—at least until morning. And now, young man,' he went on, turning back to Jamie and effectively silencing any argument, 'do as your mother says and off to bed with you, and while she tucks you in I'll start the washing-up.'

'There's no need——' Helen began, but once again

she was overruled as he disappeared into the kitchen, and she was left to trail upstairs after Jamie.

By the time she came down again the dishes were almost done. She stood just inside the kitchen door, hesitating, watching while Martyn stacked the plates neatly on the unit.

'Martyn—if you want to stay here tonight, you're very welcome,' she said slowly, and then, almost too quickly, 'The sofa's very comfortable.'

He stared at her for a moment, his eyes meeting hers, but she looked away, staring at the remains of their wine in the half-empty bottle.

'You didn't have to ask me that, Helen.'

'I know,' she said simply. 'But I don't want your death on my hands. When I think about the state of that boiler——'

'Forget the boiler!' he ordered roughly. 'That's the nicest thing you've said to me all evening!'

She managed to meet his eyes. He was wearing that strange lop-sided grin again. 'You'll stay, then?' she asked.

He was silent, almost as though he was hesitating. 'No,' he said at last. 'I think it would be safer if I left, don't you?'

And before she could ask him what he'd meant he had folded the tea-towel over the drainer and brushed past her into the hall.

She hurried after him to dive into the hall cupboard. 'Here,' she said, 'take this——' and she handed him an umbrella. Their fingers met, and before she could withdraw his hand had covered hers, and suddenly the small hall seemed very claustrophobic.

'Are—are you sure you'll be all right?' she asked awkwardly. 'It's a cold night——'

'I'll be fine,' he assured her. 'How could I be

otherwise with that magnificent dinner of yours inside
me to keep me warm?' He was standing very close,
and she could almost feel the warmth of his body
under the fine wool of his jumper, smell the heady
male scent of him mingling with that delicious cologne.

Then he said very softly, 'You've saved my life
tonight, Helen.'

Whether it was his closeness, or something in his
voice, she wasn't sure, but her heart seemed suddenly
to be beating much too loud. Why did she get the
feeling he wasn't talking about the fire? But even as
she stared up at him with wide, questioning eyes, his
mouth had brushed hers in a brief, tender caress.

'I'll see you tomorrow,' he said, and was gone.

She waited until she saw his dark figure striding out
of sight towards the Folly, umbrella overhead, and
then she shut the door with a snap and went back to
the empty living-room, to flop on to the sofa and stare
broodingly into the fire.

The Folly felt different already, Helen realised, as she
sat on the old wooden drainer in the kitchen, legs
dangling and an old scarf tied over her hair. Her
shadow from the sunlit window behind her stretched
out across the tiled floor to where Martyn sat making
notes at the big kitchen table, a steaming mug of coffee
at his elbow.

She had been dubious about coming up here this
morning after that emotive farewell last night, but she
needn't have worried. Martyn had been very business-
like this morning, and anyway, they'd been so busy
that there'd hardly been time to think—let alone
anything else! Now, at last, the kitchen looked reasonably presentable again—except for the ceiling and the
floor in front of the boiler where the tiles would

probably have to be replaced. She'd even managed to light the boiler; she could hear the water clanging and gurgling its way through the pipes as the ancient system began to warm up, and somehow it had seemed perfectly natural being here, in this house, with Martyn.

She watched him over the rim of her own cup. She had caught herself staring at him a couple of times, watching the strength in that perfectly proportioned body of his as he pulled the heavy furniture effortlessly back into place, the way the muscles of his shoulders rippled under his shirt. . .

'Don't let your coffee get cold,' she said, bringing her thoughts to an abrupt halt, and he looked up, his eyes narrowing for a moment against the aura of sunlight that surrounded her.

'I'll drink it upstairs,' he said. 'You'd better bring yours as well.'

Her feet were suddenly still, and the look on her face brought a twitch of something that could have been amusement to the corner of his mouth—except that his eyes didn't seem at all amused.

'Don't worry, Helen, I have no intention of accosting your virtue!' he mocked with a hint of sarcasm. She was immediately on the defensive, but he continued abruptly, 'We'll be going up to the bedrooms— but only to look at the floorboards!'

'The floorboards?' she echoed, surprise robbing her of what she had been about to say, and Martyn's mouth twisted as he indicated the notes.

'I want to go through the house and make a list of all the things that need doing to this place to make it habitable,' he told her. 'Then later on I can get a professional in to see how much it's all going to cost, and whether or not it's going to be worth my while.'

Her feet were still again. 'What do you mean, whether it's going to be worth your while?' she asked, frowning at him as he took a gulp of his coffee, and he watched her through narrowed eyes.

'I mean just that,' he said, and then, as his cup came down on the table again, 'This place is going to cost a hell of a lot to do up, Helen. I want to know whether it's going to be worth my while paying out that kind of money—or whether I'd be better off simply putting the house on the market.'

'You mean—*sell* it?' she asked incredulously. 'But—but you can't do that!'

His eyebrows rose. 'Why not? It's my house—and you must have known that there was always a possibility it would be sold.'

She had slid off the drainer. Now she thrust her hands into the pockets of her jeans and turned to frown out of the window. This was a possibility she had hardly even considered, and, to her surprise, one that she wasn't even sure she liked.

'Yes,' she said slowly, 'you're right. But that was before I knew it was you who had inherited the Folly——'

'You knew it would be one of the family,' he interrupted. 'Why should I be any different from the rest? And last weekend you were calling all of us fit to burn!'

'I always thought you were fond of this house——' she began, then stopped abruptly, biting her lip. 'I thought there was a possibility that you'd sell the Lodge,' she amended hastily. 'But not the Folly itself.'

'Nine years ago I wouldn't have hesitated to sell the Folly!' he declared in a voice that was suddenly harsh. 'And anyway, what does it matter to you? You'll be leaving here soon—going back to your married home!'

She swung back to face him. 'My married home?' she echoed in astonishment. 'What are you talking about?' And now it was his turn to stare at her, his eyes narrowed and piercing.

'I must admit I was surprised to find you here last weekend,' he told her. 'But when you told me about Sarah's death I naturally assumed you were here to tidy up her belongings, and then you'd be returning to your own home.'

'But this is my home!' Helen declared in bewilderment. 'After Simon's death Mother persuaded me to bring Jamie back to Sayton's Folly, and we've lived here with her ever since—but you know all that, surely?'

'On the contrary, the last I heard you'd left Sayton's Folly and you were living with Simon!' He was still watching her, and Helen stared back at him incredulously.

'But I don't understand any of this!' she exclaimed, running her fingers through her hair in agitation. 'I don't even understand why you didn't know about Mother's death! Mr Winstanley wrote to the family specifically to——'

'If he wrote to me, I certainly haven't seen the letter!' Martyn grated, and stood up abruptly. 'And as I've already told you, I've been out of the country.'

'But you have a home in London!' she contradicted fiercely.

'Correction—I have a house in London.' There was the same cold, hard edge to his voice that she'd noticed last weekend.

'Even so,' she persisted, 'you gave me the deliberate impression that you'd driven up from London last weekend——'

'And so I had.' A muscle jerked in his cheek as he

came to the sink to turn the tap on and rinse his cup
under it with hard, unreadable eyes. 'I have a career
now, Helen,' he told her harshly. 'That is, a career
outside the family firm. I paint portraits. It's not
exactly the creative paradise I envisaged in my youth,
but I happen to be very good at it, and a lot of very
rich people pay me a lot of money to do it. I travel to
wherever the work takes me, and it certainly pays the
bills. Last weekend I'd just finished a commission in
France—ahead of schedule, as it happens. I arrived in
London on Saturday afternoon, drove straight to the
house——' He stopped abruptly, and turned the tap
off with such force that Helen stared at him in concern.

'Well, I won't bore you with unnecessary details,'
he continued tautly. 'But suffice it to say I jumped
straight back into my car again and drove down here,
to be met by—you.'

He turned back to her then, almost as though he'd
just remembered she was there. 'Does that answer
your question?' he asked, eyebrows raised. 'Perhaps if
I also tell you that I've been in France for the last
three months, and in that time I've had hardly any
correspondence from London, it will help to enlighten
you. In fact, as I said before, I only heard about
Gerald's death just over a week ago.'

'I see,' said Helen, not really seeing at all. If what
he said was the truth—and she could hardly doubt
him—it seemed that he had no more idea of what was
happening at the Folly than she had. He didn't even
know that they had been told to leave the Lodge! But
one question burned in her mind above all others—if
he hadn't given the order for them to leave, who had?

'Well, I'm glad we've sorted that little problem out,'
Martyn declared, and strode back to the table to pick
up his notes. 'And now, if you've finished your coffee,
shall we go upstairs?'

CHAPTER FIVE

SOMEHOW the mood had changed. There seemed to have been a subtle, almost invisible shift in their fragile truce, and, walking round the first floor of the house with Martyn, Helen began to feel edgy, almost nervous. Down in the kitchen she had felt safe, but up here, alone with him in this house that held so many memories for both of them, she began to realise how vulnerable she was.

She looked across at him. Did he feel it too? She studied his face, but he seemed to be concentrating completely on the job in hand. They were inspecting the bedrooms, and she had the notebook now, jotting down his comments as he inspected window frames, tapped walls, and checked floorboards. Most of the rooms were still shrouded in the dust-sheets that had been spread over everything after Gerald's funeral, but knowing the house as she did she couldn't help noticing where one or two things had already been moved. Martyn was stamping his personality on the place already, she realised.

He was using the main bedroom. The bed had been made up—he'd obviously remembered where the clean sheets were kept—and there was a small mirror and elegant blue shaving-bag on the shelf in the adjoining bathroom.

'It's pretty dismal, isn't it?' he declared, as they both surveyed the ancient cast-iron bath with its splayed feet and exposed pipes. 'It might fetch a fortune at Sotherby's, but I don't fancy taking a bath in it—not in here, anyway.' He looked round in disgust at the faded Victorian wallpaper and the bare linoleum on the floor.

Helen stood just inside the door. 'Gerald never used this suite,' she told him flatly. 'This side of the house gets the wind in winter. He preferred one of the bedrooms at the back.'

'I'm not surprised,' Martyn muttered caustically. 'Everything seems to have deteriorated a hell of a lot in the last nine years.'

'It's not that bad,' she said defensively.

'You mean there's worse to come?' His eyebrows rose, and Helen began to feel irritated by his tone.

'It depends what you're used to——' she began.

'Well, if this is what Gerald was used to, he must have led a pretty miserable existence!' he said forcibly.

'Gerald was an old man, but he certainly didn't live in misery!' she retorted crisply. 'He had his little comforts, just like everyone else. It's just that he preferred to spend what money he had on keeping the estate together——'

'Then he was an eccentric old fool!' Martyn interrupted acidly. 'He would have been better advised to sell this place and move to somewhere smaller. At least then he could have ended his days in comfort!'

'He was comfortable here!' she snapped, two flags of angry colour in her cheeks now. She felt that in some way he was criticising the way Sarah had looked after his uncle—and anyway, what right did he have to pull Gerald to pieces like this when he hadn't even been near him these last nine years? 'It may seem eccentric to you, Martyn, but he loved this place——'

'And what good did it do him? The place is falling into ruin!' he declared bitingly. 'It'll take a fortune to set it to rights!'

Helen had had enough. 'What did you expect—gold taps and Sèvres porcelain?' she flung at him, and swung abruptly towards the door.

'I didn't know what to expect!' he countered in that same acid tone. 'That's one of the reasons I'm here. The way Gerald felt about me, for all I knew he could have left me a pile of rubble!'

'Well, as you said before, you can always sell it!' she snapped from the doorway. 'That way you won't be out of pocket, will you?' She walked stiffly along the landing to the top of the stairs and stood there, quivering with anger. He was as mercenary as ever! she fumed. Gerald had left him all this, and yet he was criticising the old man in such a heartless, cold-blooded way. . .

She heard him walk out across the landing and come to stand behind her.

'How do you know I've got the money to keep this place going anyway?' he questioned harshly, and she took a deep, steadying breath.

'I don't, of course,' she got out. 'When I knew you, you didn't even have a job! And as you pointed out so realistically before, I'm leaving here soon anyway, so really it's none of my damn business whether you've got the money or not, is it?' And she thrust the notebook at him and made to go down the stairs, but he caught her wrist and swung her round to face him.

'For heaven's sake, Helen, why are you so damned defensive?' he bit out. 'Gerald may have been my uncle, but you above anyone should know how I felt about him—especially after the way he betrayed me with Simon! And for all he used to let me stay here when I needed a bolt-hole from my father, you know damn well that he hated my guts! It wouldn't have surprised me in the least if he'd left Sayton's Folly to you and your mother—if only to stop me getting my hands on it!'

'Unc—Gerald knew where his duty lay!' she amended, struggling to free her wrist, but his grip was firm. 'And as for what he did—that only goes to prove what a kind and generous man he really was! That money, Martyn—the money you seem to think was some kind of bribe to Simon to marry me—was actually a wedding present! A gift to both of us—so that we could put a deposit on a flat!'

'You're too loyal, Helen!' he grated harshly. 'Tell me, is that why you ditched me the way you did? Because you knew Gerald considered me a wayward lout—and Simon was already making a name for himself in computers?'

'Don't be ridiculous!' she snapped, freeing her wrist at last. 'Your uncle had nothing to do with what happened between us—except when he tried to warn me about what a fool I was making of myself, and he was right! It wasn't me who ditched you, it was you who ditched me—because you had more lucrative possibilities open to you in London!'

'You know why I had to return to London,' he bit out. 'And you said you'd wait!'

'I did wait!' she cried, feeling suddenly ridiculously close to tears. 'I waited almost until——' She stopped, biting her lip, then swung away from him again to stare bleakly down the stairs. How could she explain? How could she tell him she'd waited as long as she'd dared?

'What's the point of arguing about this now?' she sighed, struggling to keep her voice level. 'It was nine years ago, Martyn, and it's all dead and gone—just like Uncle Gerald!'

'Is that what you think?' His voice seemed softer, huskier. She felt his hands on her shoulders and then

he turned her round to face him again, tilting her face
up to his, and a quiver ran through her as he brushed
his thumb across her damp eyelashes.

'I don't think it is, Helen, and if you're truthful with
yourself, you don't either. Don't think I didn't see the
way you were watching me earlier, and last night—I
was almost beginning to think you were softening a
little. . .' He paused, watching her, his eyes very dark,
very intense, very close. 'It may be nine years, Helen,
but we're still the same people inside. A little older
maybe, and a little more frayed around the
edges. . .but otherwise. . .'

His eyes held hers, darkening almost as she watched,
and then, before she could move or speak, his mouth
had come down on hers, not in the tender kiss of last
night, but fierce and demanding and brutally passionate, deliberately arousing all those long-lost emotions
she had tried to tell herself were dead and forgotten.
She swayed against him, and would surely have fallen
down the stairs if he hadn't held her so tightly, but it
seemed hardly to matter. She was clinging to him now,
pressing herself against him. . .

She was released, and she almost fell back against
the banister, dazed and breathless.

'Tell me now that there's nothing between us,
Helen,' he demanded huskily, and his breathing, too,
seemed unsteady.

She stared at him mutely for a moment, then
abruptly pushed him forcefully away and turned and
began to run down the stairs, holding tightly to the
banister rail for support. She was angry; bitterly,
furiously, painfully angry! Both with him and with
herself for getting into this situation, for letting this
happen——

'Running away again, Helen?' His voice came from

above her now, harsher, and with a hint of mockery in
its depths. 'Tell me, is it something in me that frightens
you—or something in yourself?'

She stopped then and turned back to look up at him,
her face hard and set. 'I have a clear conscience,
Martyn,' she told him, her voice icily derisive as it
echoed round the vast emptiness of the hall. 'And I'm
certainly not frightened of you—I know you too well!
But now that you've satisfied that over-inflated ego of
yours I have to leave. It's nearly lunchtime and I have
a son to care for—remember?'

She had already turned to continue down the stairs,
but he questioned abruptly, 'You haven't left him
alone all morning?'

She stopped, turning stiffly back to face him. 'Of
course not! He's been at Hall Farm.'

His face changed. 'He's staying with his
grandparents?'

She stared at him. 'Simon's parents moved to
Australia. It's a family called Thompson who live there
now!' And then, 'Are you telling me you don't know
anything about that either?'

But he seemed hardly to be listening. He was silent,
staring at her, his face unreadable. Then he said
slowly, 'So you and Jamie really are alone here?'

It was more a statement of fact than a question, and
it took Helen completely by surprise. It shook her,
too, the way he said it.

'I've told you, Martyn, we can take care of ourselves!' she answered forcibly. 'Jamie and I don't need
you or anyone else!'

'Perhaps not—but you need Sayton's Folly!' He
stared down at her. 'You don't have anywhere else to
go—do you?'

His eyes were locked with hers, and she glared back,

her own eyes brilliant with anger, surprise, resentment. . . But she couldn't deny it. His question might have been a shot in the dark, but her face had given him his answer, and suddenly he had taken a couple of steps towards her.

'Then stay here, Helen!' His voice was no longer harsh, but coaxingly soft. 'Why leave? You're as much a part of this place as Gerald was—and you don't need to ask for any favours, Helen. The Lodge is yours for as long as you need it. Stay here——'

'With *you*?' She glared at him for a moment, her tone indicative of her feelings, then swung abruptly to continue down the stairs, but he was closer than she realised and his hand shot out to her shoulder, holding her just below him on the stairs.

'Why not with me?' he demanded huskily.

She was incredulous. 'After what's happened?'

'That was nine years ago, Helen,' he murmured, his breath on her hair. 'And weren't you telling me just now that the past is dead and gone?'

'And just now?' she questioned derisively, and turned to glare at him again, but that was a mistake, as she soon realised. She was surprised to discover just how close he was—too close, and she had to look up to meet those dark, penetrating eyes. They seem to fill her whole vision, almost mesmerising in their intensity. . .

'I won't apologise, Helen,' he murmured huskily. 'What happened was out of my control—as it was out of yours too. There's something between us—there's always been something between us, and it's as strong now as it ever was. You can deny it to me, but you can't deny it to yourself. . .'

She stared up at him, her own eyes dark now, velvety blue, almost luminous in the strange half-light of the hall. She was remembering another time when she had stood here like this with him, his hands on her shoulders, gently caressing, his voice coaxingly soft. She had trusted him completely, gone with him willingly, trembling with excitement. . .

'Have dinner with me tonight, Helen,' he demanded thickly.

His voice brought her back to reality. 'Dinner——?' she echoed dazedly.

'I'll pick you up early so Jamie won't get too tired. . .'

Her body stiffened under his fingers, and now her eyes had lost their soft luminosity and hardened to cut sapphires.

'I hate to disappoint you, Martyn, she muttered caustically, 'but I already have a dinner date for this evening!' It gave her a great deal of satisfaction to tell him that, and she stepped away from him as she spoke, shaking his hand off her shoulder. With one last, fiercely triumphant glare, she swung away from him again to continue down the stairs, but she'd only just reached the bottom before his voice came again.

'Helen—wait!'

She stopped, her back still rigidly towards him, one hand curled tightly over the banister rail.

'What time will you be back?'

'What——?'

'We still have the downstairs rooms to inspect.'

His voice sounded almost casual now, and she turned to face him incredulously. 'You expect me to come back here this afternoon after what's happened?'

'Forget the rest of the house; we can do that another day, but there's something I want you to see.'

'Your *etchings*?' she derided acidly, and was surprised to see his mouth twitch into something like a grin.

'It won't take long.'

She lifted her wrist to look pointedly at her watch. 'Jamie has to be in Kingsleigh in half an hour for his swimming lesson,' she declared, her voice icily abrupt.

'He'll be there.' Martyn was already coming down the stairs towards her again, hands thrust into his pockets, his eyes fixed on her flushed, angry features. 'I can always take him in the Porsche——'

'*Martyn!*' He was teasing her, she realised vaguely, recognising the old familiar hint of lightness in his voice, but paradoxically that knowledge only served to make her even more angry, and she rounded on him furiously, a biting retort on the tip of her tongue, but he had reached her by now and already taken her arm to lead her firmly across the hall towards the dining-room. Through the long windows at the far end, and they were in the conservatory. Just over the threshold she was released, and she looked around, suddenly unsure what to expect.

When she'd been a child, this place had been full of fascination for her. Hot and steamy from the many exotic plants that Gerald had kept in here, it had been full of damp, shady places to play and hide.

Now it was almost bare. Most of the ferns and palms and others that she remembered had disappeared long ago, and just a few straggling, faded specimens remained as a reminder of its former glory.

She saw now that these too had been pushed to one side, and one of the tables from the sitting-room had been pulled into the centre. Up to now she had seen nothing of any brushes or paints or other artists' paraphernalia around the house and she had simply assumed that Martyn hadn't brought anything with him; but in the past he had never moved far without a sketch-pad of some kind, and she had begun to think that that strange outburst of emotion in the kitchen earlier had something to do with his career—that he was worried about his painting in some way, that he had some kind of block—but she saw now that this wasn't the case.

The table was covered by a cloth, and the cloth itself was covered—by sheets and sheets of paper torn from an artist's block, and as she approached, Jamie's face leapt out at her. Jamie smiling, Jamie solemn, Jamie with Rags, Jamie sitting cross-legged. . .

They were pencil sketches in the main, but the life and movement in them was incredible.

Martyn was still standing where she had left him, hands thrust into his pockets again, watching her. She turned to him, her face eloquent of her emotions.

'Martyn, they're beautiful!' she exclaimed.

He came to the table then, picking up one or two sketches and surveying them through narrowed eyes. 'One of the reasons I wanted to come back early from France,' he began, 'is because I have an exhibition coming up in a couple of months—an exhibition that up to now I've been in no way prepared for.'

He left the sketches to walk away from her, to look out of the glass at the fields that stretched away in front of the Folly.

'This last year or two, Helen, for the first time in my life, I'd begun to doubt my ability as an artist. That creativity in me that I'd always considered to be indestrucible—that I thought was mine by divine right—seemed to be drying up. I tried everything, but nothing seemed to inspire me. I was dissastisfied with everything I did—I was even seriously considering chucking it all in, can you believe that?' He half turned towards her and she stared back at him, her eyes wide and dark.

So she hadn't been far out when she'd wondered if it was something to do with his career that was bothering him, she thought. She remembered him having the occasional mental block with his painting in the past, but nothing serious, nothing like this. Even from this distance she could almost feel the tension in him, the vulnerability.

'When I heard about Gerald's death,' he continued, 'I knew I had to come back here. If anything could save me, this place could. There's always been something special about it, a kind of—tranquillity. . .' He paused. He was staring out of the window again. 'Perhaps it's something in the light,' he continued after a moment. 'But you feel it too, don't you, Helen?'

She nodded dumbly.

'Anyhow, whatever it is, it's worked its magic for me.' He turned back to face her. 'I did most of those sketches last night after I'd left you.' He nodded towards the table. 'There's something about Jamie, something in his face, something that's so indefinable. . .' He paused again, before continuing firmly, 'I want to do a portrait of him, Helen. Perhaps two or three for my exhibition. But I need your permission.'

She was silent, staring down at the sketches.

'It'll mean my seeing quite a bit of him—perhaps an hour every evening.'

'You can't work from memory?' she asked, without looking at him.

'No, not with this. It's too special.'

She was silent again, her face bent over the sketches, hidden from him. And inside her emotions were tearing her to pieces. *Oh, lord!* Did he know? Could he feel something between himself and Jamie—that indescribable something that she, as Jamie's mother, had always felt—or was this simply another way to get at her?

She swallowed painfully. 'You know how I feel about you and Jamie.'

He had come to stand beside her. She could feel his breath on her neck.

'I know.'

She straightened, lifting her eyes up to meet his, searching his face. His art had always been the most important thing in his life. Did she have the right to deny him this—to deny *either* of them?

'Very well,' she said at last. 'If it's so important to you—but you must ask Jamie yourself. If he says yes, then you have my permission.'

She had expected a whoop of glee, a grin of satisfaction, but there was nothing. Instead his hands came up to her shoulders, holding her in front of him.

'You won't regret it, Helen,' he told her softly. 'And don't worry, I'll take good care of him.'

Like you did with me? she thought with a stab of pain. What in heaven's name was she letting herself in for? But more to the point, how on earth was she going to survive when it was all over?

The sooner she and Jamie left Sayton's Folly, she thought despairingly, the better!

Martyn walked with her back to the kitchen while she collected the cloths and mops and the bucket she'd brought—was it only this morning?

'Are you sure you don't want me to pick Jamie up?' he asked.

'*No!*' She stopped abruptly, letting her breath out unsteadily as she turned to him. 'Thanks—I'll manage,' she added in a more reasonable tone. And then, almost as an afterthought, 'Do you still want someone to cook and clean for you while you're here?'

His eyes narrowed. 'Why, do you have someone in mind?'

'I might do.' She'd almost forgotten about the scarf round her hair, and she put her hand up now to pull it off, shaking out her hair as she did so. It fell across her shoulders and round her face like a golden curtain.

'Why don't you take a walk to Hall Farm and have a word with Liz Thompson?' she continued. 'She might be interested. She's a good cook, and I know she's fed up being stuck in the house all day while her husband works the farm.'

'I might just do that.'

Something in his voice brought her eyes back up to his face. He was staring at her hair, but even as he put his hand up, as though to touch it, she stepped back and away from him, her face cool and untouchable.

His eyes met hers.

'Come out with me tomorrow, Helen,' he murmured huskily. 'We'll go to Delamere Forest, to Hatchmere. Remember when we used to go there years ago?'

She stared at him, her eyes dilating into dark pools. Oh, yes, she remembered! She remembered hot summer days spent lying under the cool shade of the trees while Martyn sketched, and his dark face, outlined against the sun, laughing down at her; and she remembered, too, the way he would throw down his sketch-pad, and the look in his eyes as his breath mingled with hers, inflaming already aroused desires that seemed to send her into shivers of ecstasy whenever he so much as looked at her. . .

Abruptly she shut off the treacherous memories, at once horrified at the path her thoughts had been taking, and shaken by their intensity. 'I'm busy tomorrow,' she blurted. 'I have some work to do for Monday.'

'Running away again, Helen?' His mouth was twisted into that wry, lop-sided grin.

'Of course not!' she denied, hating him now.

'Then come with me. Jamie will love it.'

She hesitated then, biting her lip.

'We'll take a picnic,' he persisted, in that same husky tone. 'And we'll call somewhere for a meal on the way home. It'll go some way towards repaying you for what you did for me last night.'

'It'll probably rain again tomorrow——' she began.

'Well, if it does. . .' He shrugged, an almost careless gesture of dismissal. 'But if it doesn't. . .' He paused, leaving the sentence hanging in mid-air between them, while his eyes were still fixed on her, very vivid, very intense. 'I'll pick you up at eleven.'

She opened her mouth then to tell him no, she wouldn't go, she didn't want to see him; but somehow the words wouldn't come. She hesitated again, then picked up the bucket and walked out into the court-yard, feeling those grey eyes on her all the way until she turned the corner of the house.

CHAPTER SIX

THE dinner that evening with David couldn't have been more of a contrast to the evening before with Martyn. From the beginning Jamie seemed sullen and moody, and spent all his time sprawled over the full length of the sofa, glued to the television. He refused to be shifted, even when it was time for their meal, and Helen went to turn the set off, standing in front of it and glaring at him.

'You're not too old to be spanked!' she hissed at him, but he didn't even bother to answer. He went to sit at the table in silent defiance, his face set and mutinous.

He hardly spoke two words to David all evening, but David didn't seem to notice. In fact he hardly seemed to notice Jamie at all. He spent the whole meal talking about estate agents' fees and the price of houses, and by the end of it Helen felt fraught and irritable.

At last she packed Jamie off to bed.

'It's too early,' he complained, but she was in no mood to argue, and she could hear him banging about in his bedroom even after she'd finished the dishes.

David was in the sitting-room, still talking, and she realised guiltily that she'd hardly heard a word he'd said.

'. . .And so I thought we'd start tomorrow,' he finished, as she went to sit down, and she looked up quickly.

'Tomorrow?' she asked blankly.

He looked faintly surprised. 'Yes, tomorrow. We have to start looking at houses some time, Helen, and the sooner the better.'

'We?' she asked cryptically. 'David, I thought I'd told you——'

'Yes, Helen, I know what you said,' he interrupted impatiently, 'but this is something you'd be unwise to go into alone. You need advice, and I know one or two people who could be of help——'

Helen sat back, wishing she had a drink. 'Tomorrow isn't a good day,' she interrupted shortly, and once again David's face wore that slightly surprised look.

'What did you say?'

'Jamie and I might be going for a picnic tomorrow.'

'A picnic—in this weather? Helen, it's been raining almost all weekend——!'

'It was Martyn's idea,' she interrupted again, and now there was a short silence.

'Martyn Sayton—from the Folly?' He seemed almost incredulous, and Helen sighed inwardly. She was handling this very badly, she realised.

'But—I thought you didn't like him—at least, you gave me that impression——'

'He was having some trouble with the boiler,' Helen explained patiently. 'We helped him out, and he came here for a bath and a meal. A picnic is just his way of saying thank you.'

'He came *here*?' David really was incredulous now, and Helen was beginning to feel irritated all over again.

'Of course. Why not?' she asked testily. And then, 'David, you don't seem to understand—Martyn knows this place almost as well as I do! My mother was housekeeper at the Folly, as you know, and Martyn used to come here a lot. He was very fond of my

mother,' she added softly, remembering Martyn's
shock when she had told him about her death.

'He can't have been that fond of her—otherwise
why is he evicting you the way he is?' David pointed
out stiffly, and Helen sighed and shook her head.

'I don't know,' she admitted. 'In fact I'm not even
sure now that it is he who's evicting us. He doesn't
seem to know anything about it. . .'

'Don't be ridiculous, Helen!' David muttered
shortly. 'If he doesn't know anything about it, who
does? After all, he is the new owner of Sayton's
Folly—isn't he?'

'I wondered if perhaps the London solicitors could
have anything to do with it.' Helen frowned. 'Or even
perhaps——' She stopped, biting her lip.

'Even perhaps—what?' David demanded, staring at
her, but Helen shook her head again. For an illogical
moment the spectre of Jacqueline's cool-eyed beauty
had risen before her, but she dismissed it firmly. If
Martyn didn't know what was happening here, then
she certainly didn't. . .

'Well, why don't you tackle him about it?' David
said now. 'If he was as fond of your mother as you say
he was, there might be a chance he'll change his mind,
and if he's taking you on a picnic tomorrow. . .' He
paused, obviously irritated now, but Helen was silent.

There was no way she could tell David that Martyn
had already offered to let them stay, for that would
involve too many questions and too many explanations—explanations that she wasn't sure she could
give, especially with David in this mood. He was
already persisting crossly, 'You're going to have to do
something soon, Helen. You don't have much time
left. And if you're busy tomorrow, as you say you are,

then I suggest we arrange something for next weekend—it'd better be on the Saturday——'

'I'm sorry, David, but next Saturday is out of the
question,' Helen said quickly, and then, as David
looked as though he were about to explode, 'Have you
forgotten that next weekend is Penford Carnival? I
usually help on the stalls.'

David looked thoroughly deflated, and Helen
couldn't help a twinge of remorse. After all, in his own
way David was doing everything he could to help her.

'I'll tell you what,' she said now. 'Why don't we go
out a couple of lunchtimes in the week? We'll have
plenty of time—we can have a look around and then
you can come to the estate agents with me?'

He brightened. 'That's not a bad idea, Helen, and
then on Saturday night you can arrange a babysitter
for Jamie and we'll go to the Carnival Dance, like we
usually do. I'll get a couple of tickets next week. It'll
be something of a special occasion,' he added, and
Helen's eyebrows rose questioningly. 'It will be the
first time we've been out together properly since your
mother's death,' David pointed out reproachfully.

Helen managed a smile, and David sat back, his
irritation forgotten.

How could she refuse? Helen thought to herself.
David wasn't a dancer, and the Penford locals were
usually too rowdy for his taste, but at least he was
looking more like his usual self. With a sigh she got up
to switch the television on for him, for the sport, then
went out to the kitchen again to make another cup of
coffee.

The next morning dawned warm and hazy with the
promise of sun as only a June day can, and Helen lay
in bed with her eyes still closed, trying to analyse her

own confused emotions. She should be annoyed that she was going to have to go on this picnic with Martyn after all—why hadn't she said a plain 'no' yesterday?—but there was a little thrill of anticipation that ran through her whenever she thought about it, and her body felt warm with excited expectancy.

It was all those treacherous memories that persisted in surprising her, she thought hollowly. Why could she never remember any of the bad times—Martyn's bad temper, the arguments they had had? And then she realised with a pang that it was probably because there had never been any! Simon had always been happy to do what she'd wanted—and she had always been too willing to do what Martyn had wanted! No wonder Gerald had done his best to warn her—he must have *known*, known about *Jacqueline*. . .

It made her bitterly angry all over again to realise how gullible she had been, how complacent, how childishly naïve. . .!

But no matter what her feelings were, there was no doubt how Jamie felt. He was ecstatic. He came in early, bringing her a carefully carried cup of tea, chivvying her to get up and get ready, and whenever she looked at the excitement in his face she was filled with fear.

How could she tell him? How could she warn him so that he wouldn't be hurt? Martyn could destroy him if he put his mind to it—and he could destroy her too, she thought. If he should ever discover the truth about Jamie he would disappear back to London again—and probably take Jamie with him! And once the London Saytons knew about her son. . .

She had no illusions about their opinion of her—after all, hadn't she and her mother been loyal to Gerald all these years? And despite their avarice, they

were a wealthy family. She might never see Jamie
again. . .

But then perhaps she was simply being neurotic?
After all, why *should* Martyn find out about Jamie?
After all these years, he was hardly likely to discover
the truth now, was he? And even Sarah had never
guessed. . .!

No, she might have her fears about Martyn—about
his motives, about why he was befriending Jamie and
insinuating his way back into her life, but they were no
reason to spoil Jamie's happiness this morning—and
perhaps, too, this time with Martyn was just what *she*
needed—to purge herself of him completely! After all,
what was that saying about the hair of the dog? She
smiled grimly to herself as she threw back the covers
to climb out of bed. The past had dominated her life
for so long. Perhaps now it was time to free herself of
it—to free herself of Martyn once and for all! Because
soon she and Jamie would be leaving Sayton's Folly,
leaving the trees and the fields, and leaving Martyn. . .

They were ready and waiting with a bulging hamper
when he arrived in the Porsche. The powerful car
purred to a halt and they climbed in, Jamie in the back
seat with Rags, Helen in the front, while Martyn
stowed the hamper away in the back, joking with
Jamie while his eyes took in the simple sun-dress
Helen was wearing. His eyes came up to hers, but she
looked away, fiddling with her seatbelt, and then the
next moment the breath caught in her throat as his
hands covered hers and she felt his breath on her
cheek as he adjusted the seatbelt for her.

'Thanks,' she muttered awkwardly, and saw his
mouth twist into that now familiar lop-sided grin. Then
he had shut the passenger door securely after her and
was walking round to the driver's side, sliding his long

length into the seat next to her, and they were accelerating away up the lane.

They drove in silence, each busy with their own thoughts—except for Jamie! He sat almost between them, an arm across each of their seats, talking first to Martyn, then to Helen, telling her about the car, and it didn't seem to bother him that he only got a murmured 'yes' or 'no' in response.

Once or twice Martyn threw her a knowing grin, and she managed a smile in return, and then they were approaching the forest. Almost as soon as Martyn had parked the car, Jamie was out of it and shooting off into the trees with Rags.

'Jamie, don't go too far ahead!' Helen called, and would have started after him if Martyn hadn't caught her hand, holding her back.

'Leave him,' he told her gently. 'He's old enough to know what he's doing. If he does get too far ahead and gets lost—well, then, he'll know not to do it again, won't he?'

Helen was still staring after Jamie. 'I suppose you're right,' she murmured uncertainly, then turned as Martyn handed her jacket out of the car.

'You worry about him too much,' he said softly, slipping the jacket across her bare shoulders. 'He's a boy, Helen. He needs his freedom sometimes, just as you need yours.'

He was standing very close, his hands still on her shoulders, firm and warm. She looked up at him, but the sun was behind him, dazzling her.

'I'm surprised you've never married again,' he said, in a strange voice, and she blinked up at him. 'Or is it simply that you loved Simon too much?'

Surprised, she could only stare at him.

'Does it still hurt to think about his death?' he

probed, his voice deep and husky, and now she began
to understand. So that was what he thought, was it?
That she'd loved Simon to the exclusion of everything
else?

'No,' she said, 'it doesn't hurt.'

'But you still think about him?'

'Martyn—I've told you, the past is dead and gone.'

'Is it?' His voice told her otherwise.

'You know it is!'

He shook his head, and his hands slid caressingly
down her arms. 'What you really mean, Helen, is that
it's none of my damn business!' and his mouth twisted
wryly. 'You never give me any breaks, do you? I often
wonder what's going on inside that head of yours.'

It was relief, Helen told herself, relief that he wasn't
going to question her too much about Simon that was
making her heart beat so loudly she was sure he could
hear it! And she pulled away from him slightly, but he
wouldn't let her go completely. His hand still held
hers.

'I'll tell you what's going on inside my head,' she
said lightly. 'I'm thinking that if we don't go after
Jamie soon, we're going to have to spend the whole
afternoon looking for him!' and she tugged impatiently
at his hand. 'Are you coming?'

'Do I have a choice?' He grinned that familiar grin,
and she laughed now and pulled him up the path Jamie
had taken.

Martyn had parked in the trees at the side of the
road, and they followed one of the main pathways
through the forest before branching off towards the
Mere. This path was narrow and twisting, steeply
graded in places, then it levelled out, following a
swiftly flowing stream through willows and ancient
twisted oaks in sunlit groves, to the very edge of the

Mere itself. The ground was damp here, almost like a marsh, and it moved under their feet, making them realise how thin the layer of moss was that separated them from the water beneath their feet; for here, the sphagnum and grass and tree roots grew right out over the edge of the Mere.

Jamie was jumping up and down, fascinated by the way the ground rippled under his feet, until Martyn told him, deadly serious, that if he wasn't careful he'd jump right through it and end up in the Mere.

Jamie stopped abruptly. 'I won't, will I?' he questioned, inspecting the moss and tussocks of grass under his feet. Then very gingerly he began to step from tussock to tussock, and Helen and Martyn collapsed with laughter.

They decided to have their picnic within sight of the car. Martyn carried the hamper from the boot while Helen and Jamie spread a huge rug over the softly cushioning bracken and bilberry. They were all hungry after their walk, and thirsty too; it was warm now, and Helen threw off her jacket before reaching for the flask of coffee she'd packed earlier. But Martyn made her put it back. He produced a cool-bag from the boot of the car, opening it to reveal chilled cans of drink, and a bottle of wine and two of the crystal glasses from the Folly.

'*Madame*. . .?' he enquired, in a mock-French accent, and Helen laughed, then applauded as the wine was opened in expert fashion. She held out her glass and he filled it, and their eyes met as he clinked his glass against hers in a silent toast.

Afterwards, their appetites satisfied, they relaxed back against the rug. Martyn insisted they finished the wine, and Helen lay on her back, staring up through the gently swaying branches of the trees, while Jamie wandered around hunting for twigs, and Martyn pulled out his sketch-pad. He'd already mentioned the portrait to Jamie, and Jamie had agreed ecstatically, as they had both known he would, asking eagerly, 'Do you want to start now?'

'I think it can wait until tomorrow.' Martyn had grinned, but now he was sketching busily while Jamie sat at the base of a tree, Rags at his feet, and Helen watched, absorbed by Martyn's concentration and the way his long fingers moved over the paper.

She had always loved watching him work. It seemed unbelievable, even now, that his father should have remained so obstinately blind to his talent. He had flatly refused to let him go to art school, insisting instead that he went to university—his exam results had been excellent—to read business studies, with the intention that he should follow his brother into the family firm, but Martyn had continued with his painting even at university, and there had been some terrible rows about it, she remembered. That final summer, as soon as Martyn had arrived at Sayton's Folly, she had recognised the brooding mix of hurt and anger that had always seemed to follow his meetings with his father, and gradually it had all come out. In a last desperate effort, Martyn had begged for some time to prove himself in the art world. He had won a commission in Europe, which he had been due to begin just as he had been called so urgently back to London, to his brother's bedside.

Helen sighed. She could remember that summer in such vivid detail. Even the emotions, the tensions that, right from the beginning, had seemed to threaten to tear them all apart. At first it hadn't dawned on her why Martyn and Simon had started treating each other like strangers whenever she had been with them, until

the day she'd gone with Simon and his father to the
cattle market in a nearby town. It had been a regular
outing for her, but this particular day it had been later
than usual when Simon had taken her back to the
Lodge, to find Martyn there, ostensibly keeping out of
the way while Gerald had entertained a couple of the
county worthies, but in reality waiting for her. After a
few cutting exchanges, Simon had left—he'd hated
any kind of scene—and Helen had rounded furiously
on Martyn, accusing him of taking his anger and
frustration about his father out on Simon, because he
knew he wouldn't fight back.

'You're always defending Simon,' Martyn had
accused in a brittle voice. 'Is it because you feel guilty
about the way you feel about me?'

Incapable of controlling a flood of emotions she'd
barely understood, and mortified because she had
recognised a grain of truth in what he'd said, Helen
had flown at him, but his arm had come out to deflect
her flailing fury, and the next moment she had found
herself in his arms.

The smouldering intensity in his eyes, combined
with the throbbing passion of that hard, masculine
body pressed against hers, had unleashed a tidal wave
of sensations that had left her almost fainting with
desire. . .

'I suppose we'd better make a move.' Martyn's voice
suddenly broke into her thoughts, and she sat up
quickly, dazed and sun-flushed. She must have been
half asleep, she realised, and turned to find Martyn's
eyes full on her, devastatingly intent. She was suddenly
still, staring at him, shaken by the intensity of his look
which somehow seemed all mixed up with the vividness
of her half-dream, but with a wry twist of his mouth
he stood up to begin packing up the picnic things, and

she pushed trembling fingers through her tangled hair
as she struggled to pull herself together. But even after
they had set off walking again, this time in the opposite
direction, memories of that long-lost summer persisted
in coming back to haunt her.

They had already decided to head for Pale Heights
at the top of the hill. It was a steep climb through open
farmland, and the view behind them was incredible.
Martyn pointed out the imposing bulk of Chester
Cathedral and the Welsh Hills, just visible in the
distance, but all Helen could think about was Martyn
standing close behind her, his breath on her cheek,
and the way his long fingers rested, almost caressingly,
on her shoulders.

Her heightened senses seemed doubly aware of him,
of his masculinity, and as they walked she couldn't
prevent her eyes from following the hard-sinewed
grace of his long strides, and noticing the dark curling
hairs just visible on his wrists and in the V-neck of his
sweater.

They reached the wood at the top of the hill and
Helen was exhausted. She flopped on to the grass at
the edge of the trees, feeling limp and damp with
perspiration.

'We'll have a break here before we head back,'
Martyn said, grinning at her, and she watched him as
he came to sit next to her, his back against a tree. He
didn't even seem to be out of breath!

'You must be fit,' she gasped, still trying to get her
breath back. 'Do you still swim like you used to?'

'Occasionally,' he told her, looking to where Jamie
was disappearing into the trees, searching for yet more
twigs. 'I have a gym at the London house. But more
often than not I go for a jog. It's more convenient if
I'm working in someone else's house. You look

exhausted,' he added matter-of-factly, and Helen pulled a face.

'Thanks very much!'

He grinned, and shifted his position slightly so that he could bend over her to gently brush the hair off her face. 'Your face is red,' he murmured with a smile. 'It must be the wine. I shouldn't have insisted you finish your glass——'

The touch of his fingers on her skin was like an electric shock. She stared up at him dazedly, eyes wide and dilated, and heard his harsh, indrawn breath as his own eyes darkened. They travelled over her hair, her eyes, her skin, with burning intensity, and came to rest fixedly on her mouth.

'No—you shouldn't——' she got out, breathless now in a completely different kind of way, but she got no further, for his mouth had come down on hers in a kiss that sent her senses reeling, and suddenly she couldn't have escaped even if she'd wanted to, for his mouth held hers, drinking in her sweetness, exploring every inch of her, and she clung to him as though for support as she was suddenly swept down into an abyss of desire that seemed to turn her very bones to water. She was gathered into his arms, crushed against him as his mouth hardened, painfully demanding, seeking a response, and her body gave it willingly. She arched herself against him, and her arms slid up to encircle his neck, holding him against her with an intensity that matched his own.

He groaned and his mouth broke away from hers to travel to the soft, vulnerable skin of her neck and throat, then further to where the strap of her sun-dress had slipped off her shoulder, revealing the sensitive skin of her breast, and she gave a gasp of delight as his lips teased and tantalised, making her writhe involuntarily beneath him.

'How can you say that it's all dead and gone?' he demanded, his voice little more than a hoarse whisper against her skin. 'Look at me now and tell me that you feel nothing inside when I kiss you—caress you. . .'

She shook her head blindly from side to side. She was incapable of speech, incapable even of thought. Aware of nothing but the touch of his hands—his mouth——

'You can't deny it,' he breathed. 'And if you do then you're deluding yourself and making a fool out of me! But it's there between us all the same—as strong now as it ever was——'

His mouth came back to hers, passionately possessive, and she pressed herself achingly against him, her fingers sliding up under his sweater to revel in the feel of bare flesh, but the next moment she heard him swear under his breath and then he was struggling to pull himself away from her.

'Martyn!' she gasped.

'There's someone coming up the path,' he groaned thickly. 'My lord, Helen, when I'm with you my sanity flies out of the window!'

His eyes were lit with a flaming intensity as he looked down at her, flushed and breathless, in his arms. His mouth came back to hers in one last fierce, hard kiss, then he was pulling her to her feet.

She looked round as if in a dream. A man and a woman were almost upon them, and obviously trying to look as though they hadn't noticed anything unusual. They smiled a greeting and Martyn gave a brief nod in return. Jamie suddenly appeared at Helen's side, with Rags. She felt him slip his hand into hers, and when she looked down at him he smiled happily up at her. She heard the woman say as she passed them, 'How sweet—obviously a loving family!' and the couple were both smiling as they went on their way.

What's happening to me? Helen thought in bewilderment. What's happened to my inhibitions? My common sense? I'm playing with fire!

'Are you ready?' Martyn's voice was deep and husky. He stood on the other side of her, his hand still on her arm, steadying her, and he'd picked her jacket up from where she'd thrown it on to the grass. 'I think it's time we headed back to the car,' he told her, his mouth twisting wryly, and she nodded.

'Great—I'm hungry!' Jamie declared, and set off in front of them, Rags at his heels.

Helen followed more slowly, still in a kind of daze, with Martyn at her side, her jacket over his shoulder. It all seemed so perfectly natural. What had the woman said? A loving family? That was how they must appear to the outside world, she supposed. But the reality was very different. Martyn was right, she was deluding herself—deluding herself into letting this happen! How could she have behaved the way she had? How could she have given in so easily?

And what about Jamie? Her eyes went to where he was bouncing along in front of them. Was she deluding him too? Had he seen Martyn kissing her? Was that why he seemed so happy?

It seemed incredible that only this morning she had been worried about him getting hurt—when it was herself she should be looking out for! she realised now. But she had thought herself so immune—so invulnerable.

Martyn's hand had slipped down her arm to her fingers, entwining them with his as they walked. She

turned to look at him, and he smiled at her, a smile
that had her senses leaping and the blood melting in
her veins.

She would have to try and talk to him, she thought
in bewilderment. Everything was happening much too
fast—events were suddenly out of her control! And
yet there were still so many questions that needed
answering. . .questions about the Folly, about the
past, about *Jacqueline*. . .!

They walked back to the car by a different route,
taking a detour around Black Lake. They stood under
the trees, staring out across the sunlit water with its
floating islands of peat and moss and white, waving
tufts of cotton grass, and Martyn put his arms round
her waist and lifted her hair to kiss her nape. It all
looked so peaceful, so serene. She turned in his arms.
He kissed her, and she kissed him back with all the
warmth and passion she had thought buried and forgotten deep inside her.

She was heading for disaster, she realised dazedly,
but at the moment she was incapable of doing anything
about it.

They drove into Chester for a meal, leaving Rags,
panting and exhausted, in the car. Jamie too seemed
tired. His eyes were heavy and he was yawning his
head off, but he still managed to eat everything that
was put in front of him, unlike Helen. She hardly
noticed what was on her plate. She was too aware of
Martyn sitting beside her, his thigh against hers, and
the way his eyes smiled when he looked at her.

'Martyn,' she began at last. 'Martyn, we have to
talk——'

'I know,' he murmured softly, and caught her fingers
where they lay next to his on the table, carrying them
to his lips and kissing them in a way that made her

senses leap. 'Come to the Folly tomorrow. Bring Jamie for his first sitting and we'll have dinner together.'

'Dinner?' she echoed, frowning. 'Martyn, I don't think——' But he put his fingers over her lips, silencing her.

'No, don't think, Helen,' he interrupted huskily. 'Follow your intuition, like you did this afternoon. It has a far more devastating effect!'

She caught her breath at the look in his eyes. 'Everything is going much too fast,' she got out shakily. 'It's almost as though we're out of control——'

'I know,' he said huskily. 'It's incredible, isn't it? That's exactly the way I feel too. It seems unbelievable that it was only last week I arrived to find you standing in the hall. . .' He kissed her fingers again, one by one, his eyes locked with hers. 'I'll never forget the way you looked that night, Helen. The look on your face——'

'That's why we have to talk,' she breathed. 'There are still too many things between us—things I don't understand.'

'Tomorrow,' he promised gruffly. 'We'll talk tomorrow.'

It was dark when they arrived home. Jamie was asleep, and Martyn carried him out of the car and up to his bedroom, before coming slowly downstairs again to Helen.

'Coffee?' she asked, but he shook his head.

'But you will stay?' she whispered, her eyes dark, and there was a wealth of promise in her voice.

His fingers tangled in her hair, holding her against him. 'I want to,' he groaned thickly. 'You'll never know how much! I want today to go on forever. I want to stretch it out and savour it——'

'Then why not?' she pleaded with reckless abandonment, and moved her hips against his. 'This is what you want—isn't it?' But his arms tightened round her, holding her still.

'If I stayed tonight I'd want to stay every night,' he moaned against her mouth, 'and it's too soon for that yet! As you said yourself, there are things between us. . .'

His words brought back a grain of sanity to her overheated senses, and she looked away, already withdrawing, but once again his arms tightened and he caught her chin, tilting her face back up to his.

'I don't want anything to go wrong, Helen—not this time!' he told her huskily. 'I don't want to lose that look in your eyes, or the way your body feels against mine——' And almost as though he couldn't help himself, his lips came down to hers in a sweet, sensuous caress, but then, with an effort, he broke away.

'We'll talk tomorrow,' he promised, 'and when this mess between us is sorted out, then I'll stay. I'll stay as long as you want me to.'

Once again his lips were on hers in a last, passionate kiss, and then he was gone.

She stood in the doorway, watching the red taillights of his car disappearing through the trees towards the Folly, then she went upstairs to put the still-sleeping Jamie to bed with trembling fingers.

CHAPTER SEVEN

'IT's too expensive,' Helen declared flatly, staring round at the peeling wallpaper and rotting woodwork.

'It's the last one on the list,' David exclaimed in exasperation, 'and the least expensive we've looked at so far! It's well within your limit—and I doubt if they'll reduce the price any further.' He looked across at the young man from the estate agents for confirmation, and the young man nodded.

'That's right, Mrs Ashley. This is a very reasonable property for the price——'

'And it would suit you perfectly,' David pointed out testily. 'It's small, yes, but there's a garden.'

'It'll cost too much to do up,' Helen said, examining the window frames. 'Look at that woodwork, David, and these floorboards look a little suspect——' She tapped the floor with the toe of her shoe. 'This place would be expensive at half the price—and anyway, I don't like it.'

'Why not?' David sounded weary now.

'It feels—claustrophobic, and there's hardly any light. The rooms seem very dark. . .' She walked to the doorway to stare out at the overgrown lawn and straggling, self-seeded annuals, and a picture flashed into her mind of her mother's immaculate borders at the Lodge.

She had her back to the two men in the room, but she could almost see the look David gave the estate agent, the way he shrugged in hopeless resignation, and the estate agent looked at his watch.

'Well, if you've made up your mind, Mrs Ashley, I have some more people to see. . .'

It was a scene that had been enacted in almost every house they'd seen so far.

Helen turned back to the young estate agent. 'Of course. Thank you for your time,' she said politely. 'We have to be getting back anyway.' She looked across at David, eyebrows raised. He nodded, and she turned and walked down the path to the gate, waiting while he muttered a few words to the young man.

He had arranged all this yesterday, apparently, and had met her with it as soon as she'd arrived at school this Monday morning. They had both had free periods after lunch, and he had declared that they would just have time to see all the houses on his list. And so they had. They had been walking round properties for the last two hours, but they had had no lunch, and now Helen felt tired and weak with hunger. She looked at her watch. The afternoon break would be almost over, but she might just have time for a cup of coffee. . .

David came down the path and held the car door open for her, and she slid into her seat, staring straight ahead, while he walked round to the driver's side.

This morning she had felt pressurised and tense, annoyed because he had arranged all this without consulting her. She hated being rushed into anything— especially anything as momentous as this, and anyhow, she already had some idea of what she wanted for her and Jamie, and she'd already guessed she wouldn't find it in Kingsleigh; but now at least David was satisfied, and now that she'd seen all the houses he had picked out for her, she felt nothing but a kind of relief. Her mind was made up, and she knew now that if she was going to leave the Lodge, then she might as well make a clean break, and the sooner she told David, the better.

He climbed into the driver's seat, but instead of starting the car he said shortly, 'I thought that last place was pretty good, Helen. It would suit you admirably.'

'David,' she interrupted patiently, 'it was very good of you to arrange all this, but now that I've seen what's on offer, I don't think I'm going to find anything in Kingsleigh that I like.'

He turned in his seat to stare at her. 'What do you mean? Helen, these are only a few of the houses——'

'I'd have more choice if I looked further afield,' she said, and now he was incredulous.

'Further afield? What do you mean by that? Helen, you've lived in Kingsleigh all your life!'

'Not quite all my life,' she pointed out. 'I had thought of looking nearer to Manchester, where I lived with Simon. I'd have more choice there—and I'd probably get the chance of a better job too. In fact,' she added, with a quick, sideways glance at his face, 'one of my old university friends still lives in Manchester. I had thought of giving her a ring, to see if she knows of anywhere. . .'

He stared at her for a moment, silent and tight-lipped, then abruptly he turned and started the car, looking straight ahead as he pulled out into the traffic.

'Your mind's made up, then?' he asked, and she nodded.

'I'm sorry, David,' she said simply. 'But I think a clean break would be better for both of us.'

'It's Martyn Sayton, isn't it?' he asked, and she turned to look at him.

'What do you mean?'

'Have you asked him about the Lodge yet?' he asked, without answering her question.

'No.'

She'd all but forgotten that David didn't know the real situation.

'Are you going to?' He threw her a quick glance. 'You would have had the perfect opportunity yesterday. I'm surprised you didn't take it. You're usually so strong and decisive—and you don't have much time left——'

'I'll handle it in my own time, David,' she told him abruptly, hoping he'd leave the subject alone. 'I can't just blurt it out——'

'Why not? That letter he sent you was pretty abrupt!'

'He didn't send it,' she pointed out. 'The solicitors did.'

'They're his solicitors!' he contradicted, and threw her another quick glance, but she was silent, and after a moment he continued more gently, 'Helen, I don't think you quite realise your position——'

'No, David, it's you that doesn't realise!'

But he continued as though she hadn't spoken, 'I called to see you yesterday morning, about the houses we saw today, but you'd already left for your picnic. Liz Thompson was walking down the drive, and I gave her a lift to Hall Farm. It seems Martyn Sayton has asked her to cook for him, and she's agreed.' He paused. 'You should have heard the way she was talking about him, Helen. I would never have believed she was already married with a family of her own! And if a woman like Liz Thompson can act as though Martyn Sayton is God's gift to women, then. . .'

'Then what?' Helen asked, suddenly still.

'Well. . .' David shifted in his seat, but kept his eyes

on the road. 'I should tell you, Helen, that apparently there's been some talk about you and Martyn Sayton in the village—Penford, I mean. There was some gossip years ago—just before you married Simon Ashley——'

'I didn't know you listened to gossip, David!' Helen interrupted, ice in her voice now.

'Of course I don't,' David muttered defensively, 'but Liz thought I knew. She was curious, that's all—and after all, Helen, she is a friend of yours——'

'So Liz told you about this *gossip*, did she?' Helen demanded, and now David looked uncomfortable.

'No, she didn't,' he answered, unable to hide the trace of regret in his voice. 'In fact, I don't think she knew the details. She wasn't here when—that is, before——' He floundered to a halt, before taking a breath and continuing more firmly, 'Anyway, Helen, the point of all this is that you should be careful. As I said before, you're a woman alone there, and this Martyn Sayton is a cool customer, by all accounts. In fact Liz told me he had a reputation in the village for being a bit wild in his youth. Of course, I know that's a long time ago—and now he's the owner of Sayton's Folly. But I also know that you and he have some kind of relationship going—you can't deny it, Helen!' This as she opened her mouth to speak. 'And, despite what you think, I'm trying to warn you. I don't want you getting into something you can't handle!'

He switched the indicator on and changed down a gear to pull into the school car park, and Helen stared rigidly through the windscreen. If only he knew! she thought. She was already into something she couldn't handle—yesterday had made her realise that. She had lain awake all last night thinking about it; thinking about Jamie, but most of all, thinking about Martyn.

She too had wanted the day to go on forever, and last night—last night she had asked him to stay, she had *wanted* him to stay. But if he had stayed, what then?

This morning, in the cold light of day, would she have hated him again? Would she have hated herself?

David was right, but he wasn't telling her anything she didn't already know. She was walking a fine line, and one slip could spell disaster. . .

Jamie raced up to the Folly almost as soon as they arrived home from school, but Helen didn't go with him. She changed and made herself a drink and finished the last of the work left over from the weekend, before finally walking slowly up the drive towards the Folly.

She had determined that she would have to try and play it cool. Yesterday had been like an incredible dream, but yesterday was over, and David's words had had the effect of a douche of cold water. Yesterday she had behaved like the teenager she had once been, but today she had returned to reality. She would be her usual self: calm, cool, controlled. . .

They were both in the conservatory, Jamie sitting happily, Rags at his feet, while Martyn worked busily on a canvas, but as soon as he saw her he threw down his brush, signalling to Jamie that he'd finished, and began to wipe his hands on a rag. The smile he gave her was already melting her defences, but Jamie was demanding her attention.

'Mum, he says I can't see it until it's finished!' he complained, and Helen managed a quick glance at Martyn.

'That's right,' she told him. 'Martyn would never let anyone see anything until it was finished. It's one of his rules, and anyway, you probably wouldn't be able to recognise yourself yet. You probably still look like a bug-eyed monster or something,' she added with a stilted smile, and Jamie pulled a face.

'Martyn told me he once did a portrait of you,' Jamie said, and now Helen's smile froze as her eyes flew back to Martyn's, and suddenly alarm bells were ringing in her head. How could he have told Jamie about that? About those long summer afternoons spent alone together at the Folly. . .

She swallowed painfully. That portrait had been almost the start of everything. It had made Sarah and Gerald suddenly begin to realise what was happening between her and Martyn, and even Simon—poor loving, trusting Simon—had sensed that she had already been out of her depth and had tried to warn her, but she had been swept off her feet by a tide of passion that even then had brooked no refusal. . .

As far as she knew, the portrait had never been finished.

Martyn was watching her, eyes narrowed. 'Jamie, come and help me clean my brushes,' he invited, and Jamie went to him eagerly. Martyn covered the canvas and showed Jamie what to do with the brushes, then left him to come to Helen, taking her arm and leading her out of the conservatory.

'Come and have a drink before Mrs Thompson serves dinner,' he said, and led her into the small room Gerald had always used as a sitting-room. He went across to the drinks cabinet, opening it to reveal an array of bottles that certainly hadn't been there this time last week.

'I've been shopping.' He grinned, almost as though he could read her mind. 'And I'm glad I took your advice about Mrs Thompson. You were right—she is a good cook, but that's all I want her to do at the moment. I don't want her touching anything else in the house until I've been over the rest of the downstairs rooms and got someone in to look at the place. And anyhow, I can't stand strangers fussing round me when I'm working. Sherry all right?'

Helen had gone to sit rigidly on the edge of the sofa. He handed her a glass, and she took it without a word. He'd even remembered what she liked to drink, she thought hollowly.

'Why did you tell Jamie about the portrait?' she demanded stiffly, and he paused, a glass halfway to his lips.

He shrugged, watching her. 'Why shouldn't I?' he asked. 'You said yourself, it's all in the past——'

'And you said you wouldn't talk to him about the past!' she interrupted tautly, voice rising. 'I trusted you, Martyn—I trusted you with Jamie! You don't seem to realise that when he's with you you have a certain kind of responsibility towards him—as you do with any child. But then, I forgot. Responsibility is a word you don't understand, do you? Responsibility towards yourself perhaps, yes, but not towards other people!'

His glass came down, untouched, on the top of the cabinet, its contents spilling over the fine wood. She thought he was going to explode, to blast her with his fury and tell her, at the very least, to get out. But he was silent, watching her with that same narrowed stare, face hard, hands thrust tautly into the pockets of his jeans.

'I thought we'd got over all this,' he said abruptly. 'I thought you'd resolved this—this distorted image you seem to have of me.'

With an exclamation she stood up abruptly and went to stand by the window, putting a hand up to her throbbing temples. He was doing it again! She'd only been with him a few minutes and already that chemistry or whatever it was between them was drawing her towards him, melting her resistance, telling her to follow her senses and ignore the warnings ringing in her head. If only he would shout at her, rant and rave and be hateful to her as he had been that first evening—it would make it all so much easier! Instead he was making her feel that it was *she* who was in the wrong, and she couldn't understand it. She'd always known she had a certain kind of vulnerability where Jamie was concerned, but that was only natural. Now it seemed she had that same kind of vulnerability with Martyn too, and it was just as strong, just as intense, just as intimate. . . Oh, lord, why did he affect her like this? Why couldn't she simply tell him to get out of her life?

He came to stand behind her. She could feel his breath on her hair, then his hands came up to her shoulders and his fingers moved gently over the little pulse that beat at the base of her throat.

'Do you really believe I'd deliberately say or do anything to harm Jamie?' he asked softly. 'He's your son.'

'For all I know, that could be the very reason why you're treating him as you are!' she countered, and felt his fingers almost imperceptibly tighten.

'You mean because he's also Simon's son?' His voice was harsher now.

'You hate Simon, don't you?' she asked, and felt him stiffen, then his fingers tightened even more as he turned her round to face him.

'No, I don't hate him,' he told her, his eyes dark now as they followed the contours of her face. 'Oh, I'll admit I did at one time,' he added, his mouth twisting in wry self-derision. 'I'll admit, too, that it still hurts when I think of how you chose him instead of me——'

'And you're trying to tell me that that doesn't affect your attitude towards Jamie now?' she derided, and pulled away from him to draw a harsh breath. 'I've told you, Martyn, I won't have Jamie hurt! You don't seem to realise how impressionable boys of his age can be—and he's already developing a kind of hero-worship for you——'

'You think I don't know that?' he interrupted tautly, 'For heaven's sake, Helen, you're talking as though I'm deliberately setting out to deceive the boy!'

'And aren't you?' she asked tightly.

His jaw hardened. 'Hasn't there been enough deception in the past to last us a lifetime?' he asked emotively, and she couldn't answer, couldn't even look at him now.

'I think you're over-sensitive where Jamie is concerned,' he continued roughly. 'Or is it because it's me he's striking up a relationship with? Either that or you're jealous of the way he follows me around?' He was watching her, eyes piercingly intent. 'Or is it that you're afraid I'll take him away from you in some way?' he concluded, his eyes suddenly narrowing.

Shaken, she swung away from him then so that he couldn't see what she was sure must be written in her face, but his hands came out to grasp her shoulders again, his fingers catching her chin, bringing her face back round to his.

'Jamie may be Simon's son, Helen,' he continued, in that same emotive tone, 'but he could just as easily have been mine—and we both know that! Do you think that knowledge doesn't affect my feelings towards him too?'

She could only stare at him, rigid now, and he continued huskily, 'Do you think I don't *know* that he could have been my son? If circumstances had been different, if you'd waited for me as you said you would?' His fingers left her chin to slide back to her shoulders, caressing now, but still holding her firmly in front of him. 'But as you so succinctly pointed out, Helen, that's all in the past. *Our* past. It has nothing to do with Jamie. He has no control over the circumstances of his birth—and I have no intention of jeopardising your relationship with him! But believe me, if he had been my son, I couldn't be more aware of my responsibilities towards him than I am now.' He paused. 'And as for any other responsibilities——' his voice had deepened '—my main priority at the moment is to give you dinner this evening, and that's what I intend to do. Are you hungry?'

His fingers were caressing the fine bones of her shoulders, exploring the hollows at the base of her throat, and it was all she could do to nod her head. Despite her troubled mind, his closeness was weaving a spell on her senses, working a kind of magic on her fears, so that she felt cocooned and safe, and her worries seemed insubstantial and groundless. . .

'I've had no lunch,' she admitted, and then suddenly she remembered why she had had no lunch, and the dire threat behind David's words returned to haunt her in full force.

Martyn's lips brushed hers, lightly tantalisingly, and she closed her eyes for a moment. It felt so natural, so right, to be here with him like this, so close to him. . .

She pulled away to move back to the sofa and take an unsteady sip of her sherry. 'I went house-hunting at lunchtime,' she told him abruptly.

'Ah, now I'm beginning to understand,' he murmured, and she looked up.

'What do you mean?'

'I knew as soon as you walked in just now that you were in a strange mood.' He moved back to the drinks cabinet to pick up his glass. 'Tell me, was it the houses you were viewing, or the person you were with, that put you into such a prickly humour?'

'How do you know I didn't go alone?' she asked, surprised and suddenly suspicious.

The corner of his mouth lifted. 'Women don't usually go house-hunting on their own,' he explained. 'Although, where you're concerned, I'm beginning to realise that anything is possible. . .' He was watching her over the rim of his glass.

'You'll be telling me next that you know who I went with!' she retorted, half probing, and his mouth twisted into the semblance of a smile.

'I can make a good guess. David Evans?'

She swung round to face him. She was silent for a moment, staring at him, then she demanded tautly, 'How do you know about David?'

One eyebrow quirked upwards. 'Shall we say—a little bird told me?'

'*Jamie!*' she erupted furiously, and swung back to pace to the window again. 'I deliberately told him not to mention——!' She stopped abruptly.

'Anything about your affairs?' he finished for her, his voice cooler now, more abrupt, and she caught her lip between her teeth. He was so close, and yet they might as well be miles apart!

'Tell me, Helen, is it just me you're trying to keep at arm's length—or is it everyone you meet?' Martyn continued, his voice harsh now. 'First you're annoyed because I told Jamie about the portrait I did of you, and now you're furious because he's told me about this other man in your life! It's as though there's a wall around you—a wall you seem determined I shouldn't breach! I can hardly believe that it was only yesterday I held you in my arms——' His voice had deepened with devastating remembrance.

She was silent, quivering, torn in two.

'Is it something to do with this David Evans?' he demanded.

Her fingers were twisted round the stem of her glass. 'Did Jamie tell you it was?'

'Jamie didn't tell me anything, but I can read between the lines!' he declared roughly, and reached into the cabinet again to refill his glass. 'I know he's worried about your relationship with him.'

Her head jerked up. 'Did he say he was?'

'He didn't have to!' He took a gulp of his drink. 'He doesn't like him, does he?'

Once again Helen was silent, and he demanded roughly, 'Have you slept with him?'

Astounded, she swung back to face him. 'What kind of a question is that?' she demanded unsteadily. 'And what gives you the right——?'

'I have no rights!' he interrupted tautly. 'At least, not where you're concerned. You've made that abundantly clear—despite the chemistry, the bond between us that you seem so intent on denying! But I'd like you to remember, Helen, that last night you wanted *me* to stay with you—and I wish to heaven now that I had!'

'Then why didn't you?' she flung at him.

'Because it's too soon!' he declared, banging his glass down again. 'The time isn't right—for either of us! But when it is——'

'When it is, you'll love me and leave me, just like you did before—is that it?' she retorted bitterly, and there was a sudden silence. His face hardened, almost as though he'd been struck, but his eyes were locked with hers, and the fire in them seemed to scorch her through to her very nerve-ends.

She looked away, staring into her sherry, but her fingers were trembling so much she was almost spilling it. She put it down jerkily on the small table. 'David is just a friend,' she muttered at last.

'Then what is it with you, Helen?' he demanded roughly.

'He—he's been very good to me, especially since Sarah died.'

'And that's why you're house-hunting with him— because you're *grateful*? Good lord, I don't understand any of this—I don't understand *you*!'

'Have you ever tried to understand me?' she whispered. 'Have you ever *wanted* to?'

His eyes jerked back to her face. 'What's that supposed to mean? For goodness' sake, Helen, I've already told you, you can stay at the Lodge for as long as you want to!'

'Yes—but on whose terms?' she demanded tautly, and ran her fingers through her hair in a desperate movement.

'You needn't worry that there'll be any strings!' he grated harshly. 'I won't try to——'

'Martyn, you don't understand!' she declared unsteadily, and drew a harsh breath. 'Everything's changed—I've changed! I'm not a child any more, prepared to follow you around like a devoted slave and swallow anything you care to tell me!' She swung abruptly back to face him. 'Do you think I'd care if we were the only two people involved in all this?' she asked unsteadily. 'Do you think I'd care whether it was an affair you wanted, or simply another summer fling?'

Martyn's face was rigid. 'Don't play with me, Helen,' he muttered warningly. 'You've told me David Evans is just a friend, and I'll accept that——'

'I'm not talking about David!' she got out frustratedly. He wasn't making this any easier for her! 'I'm talking about you, Martyn, and me—and *Jacqueline Beauford*!'

He stared at her. His brows snapped together into a black frown, and a muscle jerked in his cheek as his jaw hardened. 'What has Jackie got to do with any of this?' he demanded suddenly.

Helen turned away from him again then, staring unseeingly out of the window as a stab of pain tore through her. What had Jacqueline got to do with anything? 'I know that you were going to marry her,' she got out in a controlled voice.

There was a stunned silence.

'You're asking me if I'm married?'

'Is that so unreasonable?'

Once again there was a silence, then she heard the breath explode from between his teeth. 'For heaven's sake, Helen, do you really believe that after what happened between us nine years ago, I'd come back here and become involved with you again if I was still married to Jackie?'

Her breathing suddenly stopped. 'So you did marry her!'

'Yes, I married her!'

At the sound of those harshly spoken words, Helen suddenly felt as though the blood was draining from her body, and there was a constriction across her chest, like a great weight on her heart, but Martyn's fingers were already on her shoulders again, turning her firmly back to face him.

'But we're no longer husband and wife, Helen, believe me!' he continued harshly. 'I couldn't take another day of——' He stopped abruptly, and she stared up at him, her body rigid under his fingers, her eyes wide and dark, fixed on his face. His voice had that same cold, hard edge that she'd noticed before, and the muscles of his face were taut and angry.

'We're going through divorce proceedings,' he told her abruptly, but she didn't miss the bitterness in his voice, and even as she began to breathe again, she realised with a painful jolt that perhaps she had been right the first time after all. It was something to do with Jacqueline—with his marriage—that had carved those lines into his face. Was Jacqueline the reason, too, why he had arrived at the Folly the way he had, wanting no one to know he was here?

But the hard lines of his face were already softening, and the fierce grip on her shoulders eased as his eyes came back to hers. 'So you see, Helen, you need have no worries on that score!' he told her, with a wry twist of his lips. 'Jackie too is in the past. My past. In fact my whole London life is over, Helen. It was over even before I returned to Sayton's Folly, and then—good lord—when I arrived to find you standing in the hall that night, it was like an earthquake under my feet! I knew then that, however long I'd been away from you, nothing had changed between us. . .'

Her heart leapt. She could feel the thud of his heart under her fingers, and the look in his eyes set her senses on fire, and when his mouth covered hers she didn't resist. How could she? After all, wasn't his reassurance just what she needed to hear? And when his mouth hardened into passion she closed her eyes and relaxed against him, and relief flooded through her.

But were Martyn's reassurances going to be enough after all? she thought hollowly. Wasn't she already beginning to realise that she needed something more? Because as he had said, in some respects, nothing had changed. . .

She was in the sitting-room of the Lodge, a cup of tea going cold in her lap as she stared rigidly across at Laura Edgeworth, one of her mother's old WI cronies. She had assumed at first that she had come about the carnival, of which she was one of the leading lights and which was now only three days away, but after gazing mistily round this room, which still held so many memories of Sarah, Laura Edgeworth's eyes had come to rest worriedly on Helen.

'It's partly because of Sarah that I had to come,' she explained hesitantly. 'It concerns Martyn Sayton—and your circumstances. . .'

And Helen had known then that there was far more to it than just the carnival.

'Mrs Edgeworth, if it's about all this gossip that's going round the village at the moment——!' She was glad Jamie wasn't here to overhear the conversation. Thankfully he was up at the Folly, having another sitting; but Mrs Edgeworth, surprise in her face now, put up a flustered hand.

'Oh, no, Helen dear! It's nothing to do with that— although that is partly why I'm here——' She faltered to a halt, then pulled out her handkerchief to dab delicately at her eyes, before beginning unsteadily, 'I don't know whether you know or not, Helen, but we haven't been able to agree on who to ask to open the carnival this year?' And when Helen gave a brief nod, she continued, 'Well, it was decided—I should say, it was put forward—that we ask Martyn Sayton. After all,' she added hurriedly, 'his family have lived here for generations—and he's the last of the line, even though we have no idea if he's going to stay here or not.'

'I see.' Helen's eyes shifted to stare out of the window on to the garden, and Laura Edgeworth looked at her now with something like compassion.

'That's why I had to see you, Helen. I realise that it will put you in a difficult position.' She gestured with the handkerchief. 'All this business with the Lodge—you must feel very uncomfortable, not knowing whether or not you'll be able to stay here——'

'It's good of you to let me know.'

'I didn't want it to come as a shock. We need you on Saturday, Helen, but of course, I don't want you to feel embarrassed—and if you'd rather not. . .?'

Helen's eyes left the garden to come back to Laura Edgeworth, then slowly she bent forward to put her cup and saucer back on the tray. This afternoon, after school, she'd called at the post office in the village. She'd opened the door with its familiar bell and had been met by a sudden wall of silence as all eyes had swivelled guiltily in her direction. The two old biddies who had been deep in conversation with Mrs Jackson, the notoriously garrulous old village postmistress, had been amiable enough while she had been in the shop, but she'd hardly gone out of the door before they had been talking again, their heads nodding in her direction, and it had been all she could do to walk calmly back to the car.

But then she thought of Jamie. He could hardly wait for Saturday to come round. He was in the races. He was having a tea in the big marquee with Peter and the other village children.

'I've already entered some of my mother's jam in the home-made section, Mrs Edgeworth,' she said at last. 'I think the least I can do is see if it wins a prize, as it did last year—don't you?'

'We can count on you, then?'

Helen nodded. 'Yes.'

Laura Edgeworth's face cleared as if by magic as she reached for her own cup. 'Don't worry, Helen, everything will sort itself out,' she said comfortingly. 'And as for all the gossip that's going round—don't let it bother you. It's just unfortunate that people around here have such long memories.' She drained the last of her tea. 'They're all worried about what it's going to mean for the village, that's all, and it's understandable, really. This may be the nineteen-nineties, but most of the land around here belongs to the Folly, and if Martyn Sayton should decide to sell. . .' She paused, raising her shoulders in an expressive shrug, before adding significantly, 'The burning question at the moment is—whether or not he's going to stay!'

And that was the whole point, Helen thought hollowly as she closed the door behind Laura Edgeworth. Was Martyn going to stay? Didn't those few brief words hold the key to all her fears?

She walked slowly back to the sitting-room to flop on to the sofa again and stare bleakly at what was left of the tea and biscuits on the tray. She'd been a fool, she realised suddenly. A blind fool. She had thought she could play him at his own game—have a light, flirtatious affair—but she knew now that things had gone much too far for that, and she could delude herself no longer. She still loved him, she knew that now, and the thought of packing up, of leaving Sayton's Folly—of leaving Martyn—when the six weeks were up as she had originally intended was becoming more and more unbearable.

But what else was there for her to do? For despite what Martyn had said on Monday evening about his life in London—about Jacqueline—she couldn't forget the way he had talked about his divorce. She couldn't forget the bitterness in his voice, and it was beginning to prey on her mind like some kind of festering sore!

Hearing him say that his marriage was over, that he was going to be free, should have eased her mind, made her feel at least—*happy*, but instead there was only a hollow emptiness inside her, caused by the knowledge that he had married Jacqueline after all, so he must at least have loved her.

And from the way he had talked about her, about the divorce, it had crossed her mind more than once that perhaps he still did. . .

She closed her eyes against the pain that was like a knife twisting in her stomach. All these years. . . She had tried to forget Martyn, to build a new life with Simon—and she would have succeeded, too, if Simon's life hadn't been ended so tragically. She opened her eyes again to stare bleakly through the window. If only Simon were here now! He would know what to do. He would know exactly how to help her, advise her, protect her—protect her against Martyn!

Her eyes filled with tears as she remembered that final day at the hospital with Simon. He had been so weak by then, but she would always remember the love in his eyes as he'd looked at her, as he'd made her promise to find someone else, to marry again. . .

Oh, lord, Simon had known her so well! But Martyn knew her too, and in a completely different way. . .

She wiped her cheeks with trembling fingers. There could have been other men in her life, she knew that. It was simply that anyone who tried to get close to her was given the cold shoulder. Even David was kept at a distance—like a dog on a lead. Martyn was right: she kept everyone at arm's length. She had always told herself that it was because of Jamie—but she knew now that Jamie had only been an excuse, and she knew, too, that deep down she wanted to take up Martyn's offer to stay at Sayton's Folly. . . With him. . .

But could she? Or was she deluding herself in that too? After all, wasn't she still afraid? Afraid to trust, afraid to love, afraid that what had happened nine years ago would simply be repeated. . .?

With a harsh sigh, she sat up abruptly and began to collect up the things on the tray, before getting up to carry it through to the kitchen. So much for being cool, calm and controlled!

Even now her face filled with colour when she remembered the way Martyn had kissed her on Monday evening—the way she had kissed him. It was only Jamie's interruption, with Liz behind him, come to announce that dinner was ready, that had split them apart.

Jamie had been all smiles when he'd seen them, but the surprise in Liz's face had left her feeling hot and embarrassed—there had been no time for explanations. By the time they had finished their meal and were drinking coffee Liz had already left, and Helen had found herself wondering what Gerald would have said if he could have seen them there, in that house, the picture of family bliss. . .

The tray clattered on to the kitchen drainer. She had tried not to think of what Gerald would say—or what David would have said if he could have seen them. She wanted to shut all that out, to bury her head in the sand—but there was no way she could escape from reality.

And she had Jamie to think of. She had to do what was best for Jamie. . .

CHAPTER EIGHT

WHEN Helen went up to the Folly later, it was to find Martyn alone in the conservatory. He was wiping his hands on a rag, surveying his canvas, frowning in concentration, and she stood just inside the door, unwilling to disturb him—to break up the tranquil scene. But almost as though he could feel her eyes on him, he turned and saw her, and his eyes darkened.

'You're late!' he admonished in mock severity, and threw down the rag to come towards her. 'Jamie has already gone to wash his hands for dinner.'

She was gathered against him, and his mouth was about to come down on hers when Jamie suddenly appeared.

'Oh, hi, Mum,' he greeted her briefly, then his attention returned to Martyn. 'I've washed my hands,' he announced, 'and there's something cooking in the kitchen, but I can't find Mrs Thompson anywhere!'

'That's because Mrs Thompson isn't here this evening,' Martyn returned. 'I gave her the evening off. Why don't you go and start setting the table, and if you're hungry you can pour yourself a cola? I'll be along in a minute.'

Jamie obediently went off again, and Martyn turned his attention back to Helen.

'I hope you still like Italian cuisine,' he murmured, and now Helen felt as though her heart had suddenly stopped.

'Don't tell me you've cooked dinner yourself?' she queried, and he smiled, that familiar lop-sided smile.

'This is a special meal, Helen,' he told her softly. 'Something I had to do myself. A kind of celebration, if you like. I realised the other evening that it was the first time you and I have sat down to eat together in this house for a long time.'

But was it going to be the last time? The thought flashed into Helen's mind, and suddenly she was icy cold, trembling, remembering the last time he had cooked for her here. It had been the evening before he'd received that fateful phone call about his brother. Her mother had been ill—a summer cold—and Gerald had been out at a dinner in aid of something. She had sat for Martyn and he had worked until late on the portrait. Afterwards he had cooked spaghetti for her. They had been completely alone. . .

The memory of that last meal with him had haunted her for months, and she drew a ragged breath. Was everything happening all over again, as she had feared? Would this be their final meal together? Did he intend to make love to her, as he had done nine years ago, before finally walking out of her life?

He was frowning down at her, sensing the change in her, and jerkily she pulled away from him to go and stand where he had stood by the canvas, but she didn't look at it.

'You haven't told me how the portrait is going,' she got out unsteadily. 'Jamie has already had three sittings. Will it take many more?'

He thrust his hands into his pockets, but kept his eyes on her face. 'That particular portrait is nearly finished. It only needs one or two finishing touches.'

'And then you'll be returning to London?' It wasn't a question, more a statement of fact, and his eyes narrowed even further.

'Helen, I've already told you, I have no life in London.'

'But you still have—*business* there?' she probed unevenly, unable to avoid the emphasis. 'There's the firm, for one thing—and you told me yourself you have an exhibition coming up. No doubt there'll be things you have to—*attend* to?'

'Helen, what is this?' he demanded abruptly. 'Some kind of inquisition?' But she was silent, waiting, tautly expectant, and the breath hissed from between his teeth.

'The firm more or less handles itself—and the exhibition isn't for another six weeks yet. There are one or two things I have to see to, yes,' he admitted, 'but I have an agent in London who makes most of the arrangements for me——'

'An agent?' she interrupted quickly.

He moved his shoulders. 'He's supposed to save me time and expense worrying about the financial side of things,' he answered, but she was still staring at him, and he flicked his wrist in a dismissive gesture. 'I get a lot of work from abroad, and I need someone in this country to co-ordinate the business side of things,' he explained. 'Charles handles the details of my commissions, arranges my exhibitions, that kind of thing.'

'I see.' Just for a moment hope had risen, only to be dashed again. This man Charles couldn't possibly have had anything to do with that letter from the London solicitors.

'And—and what about your divorce?' she probed, feeling a sudden constriction in her throat. 'No doubt there'll be things you'll have to see to regarding that too. . .?' Her voice trailed into silence. He was still watching her, but now his eyes were piercingly intent.

'That too more or less handles itself—I happen to

have a very good solicitor! Helen, what is this?' he repeated abruptly, and his hands came out to her shoulders, holding her in front of him as he frowned down at her. 'Why all the questions? I've told you, my London life is over—and there's no need for you to worry about Jackie!' His frown deepened. 'Who told you about her, by the way? Was it Gerald?'

She shook her head. 'No.'

'Then who?'

'Does it matter?' she evaded, and sighed then. He was making her feel as though she was being unreasonable, and perhaps she was—neurotically so. After all, it wasn't as though she didn't *believe* him. . .

'Oh, Martyn,' she began, 'I know I always accepted your London life—I never questioned you about it—but——'

'But now there's no need to question it,' he interrupted firmly, 'because it's non-existent! It's in the past, Helen, and so is Jackie——' He paused. 'Unlike someone I could mention. . .' His voice had deepened huskily. 'You haven't told me why you were late, by the way.'

Helen raised her shoulders in a little shrug. 'I had a visitor.'

His eyebrows rose. 'Laura Edgeworth?' And now she looked up.

'She's seen you already?' she asked in surprise.

His mouth twitched into a smile. 'When I saw who was striding up the drive, I damn near dropped everything and ran out the back door!'

It was all Helen could do not to smile then too. 'Are you going to do it?'

'Is there any reason why I shouldn't?' His eyes were darkly disturbing, almost taking her breath away.

'Of course not—it's just that I thought you wanted peace and quiet, that's all.'

'I did,' he told her huskily. 'But I can't think of anything more desirable than dancing with you on Saturday night. . .' He drew her towards him. 'Unless, of course, it's dancing with you here. . .alone. . .' He fitted her body against his and his lips met hers; light, caressing, arousing an aching response in spite of her tangled emotions.

'It's a long time since I've seen you in anything other than jeans, or those prim blouses you wear for school,' he said thickly, and his eyes ran meaningfully over the slim length of her; and then, when she didn't speak, 'You will let me take you to the Carnival Dance?' he probed softly, but she looked away, hesitating, once more torn in two.

'I can't.'

'If it's because of Jamie——' he began, a smile in his voice, but she shook her head, and his eyes narrowed.

'Then why not?'

She swallowed. 'I'm already going with someone else.'

Suddenly his eyes were like flints. 'David Evans!'

She nodded, unable to look at him. She had done everything she could to get out of going to the dance with David, but in spite of everything he almost seemed to be looking forward to it, and had reminded her about it only this afternoon. He wasn't going to give up easily, she realised, and caught her lip between her teeth.

'You told me he was just a friend,' Martyn pointed out, his voice dangerously quiet.

She nodded. 'He is.'

'Then, as a friend, he'll understand if you explain the change of circumstances?'

She hesitated again. 'I can't, Martyn,' she sighed. 'I promised.'

With an exclamation he swung away from her to pace angrily to the table, bringing the palm of his hand down on it and making the tubes of paint jump; and when he turned back to her his face was hard and set and his eyes were like two dark chasms as he looked at her.

'I'm beginning to think I don't understand you at all, Helen,' he muttered tautly. 'This thing with Evans is like Simon all over again! Just what is it with you? Was I a fool to think that things could be different this time?'

His eyes held hers and his voice was deep and harsh, full of raw emotion, and she caught her breath. She wanted to trust him—oh, how she wanted to!

'You made a promise to me too, once, Helen. You didn't find it so hard to break that one.'

'I didn't break it!' she burst out.

'You're saying I did?' he demanded tautly. 'For heaven's sake, I could at least have understood it if you'd told me to my face that you didn't love me any more—or that Gerald and your mother were pushing you to marry Simon! I know damn well they didn't approve of me!'

'They didn't approve of you because they thought you were stringing me along—and they were right!' she retorted tremulously. 'You never intended to come back!'

His lips curled back into the semblance of a smile. 'That's a pretty lame excuse, Helen, and you know it! Even before I got the message about my brother you knew I'd be away at least a month.'

'I waited six weeks,' she answered chokingly. 'And you didn't even write!'

'For goodness' sake, you know what the situation was like with my father!' he exploded harshly. 'And when my brother died. . . Good grief, Helen, do you know what my father said to me at my brother's graveside—almost before his body had been lowered into the ground?' And when she could only stare at him, at the bitterness in his face, he continued tautly, 'He told me that now my brother was dead *I* was the eldest son, and as such I had a commitment both to the firm and to my family!' He laughed bitterly. 'What had they ever done for me?'

He turned away then, running frustrated fingers through his hair, his face full of painful memories, but when he turned back a moment later to stare bleakly out of the long conservatory windows, his jaw was hard and set. 'In the end I had to get away,' he continued. 'I went to stay with some friends of mine for a few days, and I decided in the end that I would take up that commission in Europe—and to hell with my father!'

'And what about me?' Helen got out in a cracked whisper. 'Was it to hell with me too?'

His back was towards her, and she could see the tension that seemed to hold every muscle rigid. Then he got out in that same taut tone, 'That was the hardest part of all, Helen. Like a fool, I wanted desperately to see you, but I was also young and afraid. I knew if I wrote or tried to contact you in any way, before my plans were finalised, Gerald would find out from your mother, and perhaps tell my father where I was staying and what I had decided—and ruin everything for both of us. So I came to see you.'

She stared at him. 'You came here? But I never saw you!'

'You weren't here. I saw Simon.'

'*Simon?*' She was incredulous. 'But—he never told me——?'

'There was hardly any point, was there?' he muttered rigidly. 'He told me you didn't want to see me anyway, that it would probably only upset you— because you'd realised that it was him you loved after all, and you'd both decided to get married as soon as possible!'

'*What?*' For a moment she was incapable of doing anything but stare at him, then she burst out in bewilderment, 'But didn't he tell you? Didn't he say that I'd already been down to London to try and see you too?'

There was silence for a moment, and then slowly he turned from the window to stare at her, his eyes narrowed and intent. 'Helen, I've already told you, there's been enough deception——'

'It's the truth!' she burst out, and then almost incomprehensibly, 'Simon was probably just trying to protect me, because he knew how upset I was after what your father had said——' She stopped abruptly. Oh, lord, it was still painful for her even to think about what his father had said about him—about Jacqueline, let alone tell Martyn about it now, when she was still so unsure. . .

But now it was Martyn's turn to stare. 'My father?' he questioned sharply, and his brows snapped together. 'You saw my *father*?'

She ran her fingers through her hair in a weary movement. 'I asked for you,' she began hesitantly, 'but you must have been with those friends you mentioned. Only your father—your father made it sound as though——'

She couldn't finish, and he swung back to the window, swearing savagely as his fist came down on the window frame with such force that the old panes rattled.

'He knew where I was all the time!' he muttered violently, and then, 'I'm beginning to understand now, Helen. No wonder you thought I'd strung you along and then deserted you—no doubt my father took great pains to explain to you that my life at Sayton's Folly was over, and that I wouldn't be returning here again?' He had turned back to her for confirmation, and even though she couldn't look at him, her face gave him his answer.

'He was ruthless, Helen. Absolutely ruthless! Gerald had his faults, but at least he loved this place— and the estate. All my father cared about was money and the continuation of the family name! He was determined to get me into the firm—to fulfil my obligations, as he saw them!'

'But you did, didn't you?' she questioned tautly, her voice barely above a whisper now. 'You did fulfil your obligations!' And now his face was bleak as he turned back to the glass.

'I could hardly believe what Simon told me that day,' he muttered harshly. 'And then, finally, I got in touch with Gerald. He confirmed you were married, and that Simon had got a job in Manchester and you'd both left Sayton's Folly. It was like the final straw,' he told her. 'You should have seen my father's face when I finally capitulated! And I certainly gave him his money's worth,' he added bitterly. 'I worked damned hard in that firm. I introduced new technology, and within two years the turnover had more than doubled. My father was rubbing his hands in glee, but things didn't quite work out as he expected. His heart gave out, and within another couple of years he was on his deathbed and I was head of the firm! It went public— and I was rich enough to do what I'd wanted to do all along!'

'And is that why you married Jacqueline?' Helen choked unsteadily, unable to keep the bitterness out of her voice. 'Are you trying to tell me that *she* was one of your obligations too?'

'I should never have married Jacqueline.'

She stared at his back. 'You're telling me your marriage was a *mistake*?' She gave a crack of something that could have been laughter. 'Oh, come on, Martyn, surely you don't expect me to believe that!'

His eyes narrowed as he turned back to face her. 'And what about *your* marriage, Helen?' he bit out. 'Are you saying that was any better? Are you saying it was true love between you and Simon—after what *we'd* done together?'

Her laughter ended as abruptly as it had begun. 'My marriage is nothing to do with you!'

'But if Simon had lived,' he persisted relentlessly. 'Would you still have been living in Manchester with him? Would you have been *happy*?'

'Simon loved me——'

'Did you love him?'

'Yes!'

'As a brother, perhaps,' he retorted, still watching her, 'but I remember the way you were with me!' His probing stare was finally too much and she swung away, but not for long. Almost immediately his hands were on her shoulders and his fingers grasped her chin, forcing her eyes back to his.

'Things have gone too far between us now for there to be any more pretence, Helen. I know it—and so do you! Simon was your bolt-hole, your safety net—and now this David Evans is following the same pattern!'

'You're exaggerating!' she derided, finding a defence in anger. 'I've told you, David is just a friend.'

'Then why were you house-hunting with him the other day?' he questioned tightly. 'Don't I at least deserve an explanation?'

'But I haven't *got* any explanations!' she burst out tremulously. 'Don't you understand, Martyn? We *have* to leave!'

His grip on her shoulders slackened. 'It's because of the past, isn't it?' he demanded, and now his voice was harsh and vibrant with emotion. 'Because of *me*!'

'*No!*'

'Believe me, Helen, I can be patient!' he declared unsteadily. 'If you need time, then I can give you all the time in the world—I won't try to force you into anything you're not ready for.'

'Martyn, you don't understand!' she cried, and ran agitated fingers through her hair. Suddenly she felt limp. She gave a ragged sigh. 'I think you'd better read this. . .'

She pulled a piece of paper out of her pocket. It was a copy of the letter from the London solicitors—Mr Winstanley had given it to her before she'd left his office that fateful morning. She held it out to him.

Martyn's eyes were questioning, but he took it from her and stood by the glass to read it, and she stood a little apart from him, watching his face.

He read it once, and then again. His head came up and he stared, almost incredulously, she thought, out towards the fields. Then slowly he turned towards her.

'When did you get this?' he demanded in a low, chilling voice.

She swallowed tightly. 'It arrived at Mr Winstanley's office almost a fortnight ago.'

'And you believed it was from me?'

She moved her shoulders in a helpless shrug. 'At first everyone thought your father was coming to the Folly,' she began, 'but then—when you arrived. . .'

She couldn't finish, and in the silence that followed his eyes came up to meet hers.

'You thought I was exacting revenge for what happened nine years ago—is that it?' he demanded in that same chilling tone, and then, when she couldn't answer, 'For pity's sake, Helen, surely you didn't think I could pull such a cruel and callous trick as this? Believe me, I didn't even know about Sarah's death until the other day!'

'I realised that. That was why I just couldn't understand. . .' Again she faltered to a halt.

His face had taken on the pale, tight quality of a man who has passed the stage of mere anger and is enveloped in a cold, furious rage. 'Hell and damnation, and when I offered to let you stay at the Lodge—you must have thought——'

He couldn't go on. Instead his eyes held hers, and they seemed to burn right through to her very soul.

'Did you find it so hard to trust me, Helen?'

She couldn't answer, couldn't even look at him now, and he swore savagely before turning abruptly to slam out to the hall. She heard the ting of the telephone in the study, and even from this distance she could hear the fury in his voice, so why didn't his reaction fill her with some kind of relief?

After all, she *deserved* Martyn's anger—she knew he hadn't sent that letter—but there was still the question of who *had* sent it.

And it was almost certainly one of the family.

But Richard Sayton was dead, and she only knew of some of the others through Gerald—and even Sarah had never met any of them personally!

But someone had known her, she realised hollowly, and known her and the Saytons' affairs well enough to instruct the London solicitors to evict her from the Lodge. . .

The phone in the study was slammed down again, and Martyn came back into the conservatory. He paced angrily to the glass to glare out, and the look on his face made her shiver, then abruptly he swung round again and his eyes met hers, and she knew he could see the questions in her eyes, the uncertainty.

A muscle jerked in his jaw. 'I've arranged for all the papers relating to the Folly to be sent directly to me here,' he bit out. 'And I'll go through them all with a fine-tooth comb. I need to know that there are no more items of crass stupidity demanding my attention!'

He came back to her then, grasping her shoulders and holding her in front of him, almost as though he was afraid she would move away.

'Remember I told you I've been out of the country?' he continued abruptly. 'I've had no correspondence from England at all—and I've heard nothing from those damned solicitors! In fact, the first I knew about Gerald's death was from a letter on Charles's desk! I haven't even seen any of the details of my inheritance, but everyone knew how fond my uncle was of your mother—of you, and I can't conceive how something like this could happen! But I'll find out, Helen, I swear to you, and so help me, when I do——'

His face was a taut mask and the breath hissed angrily from between his teeth, then his eyes came back to hers and his fingers relaxed their fierce grip.

'But you must promise me something in return,

Helen,' he murmured abruptly, and she looked up at him, stiffening.

'Promise me that this time you'll wait,' he continued. 'Give me your word that you won't leave the Folly—at least, not yet. We can make it work this time, Helen, I know we can, but you must promise me that you'll stay here, at least until everything is sorted out. I've told Charles that I want those papers here by the end of the week, and then I'll go through them all in detail—and I'll sort out this whole damn mess, Helen. I promise!'

For the last few years the sun had shone on Penford Carnival, and this year was no exception. It was a glorious day, and Helen hummed in tune with the brass band playing vigorously at the other end of the field as she was kept busy serving on the cake stall.

She was wearing the pink sun-dress she had worn the day of the picnic with Martyn, and she felt gloriously happy—and why not? she told herself firmly. Hadn't Martyn said everything would work out this time? Hadn't his words held some kind of promise for the future? And that there could be a future for them, now, she had no doubt—the happiness of these last few days at Sayton's Folly had told her that. They had spent every spare moment together, and the promise in Martyn's eyes when he looked at her, the happiness in Jamie's face when he looked at them both, had banished any shadows, any spectres from the past that had persisted in haunting her.

After all, Martyn had been right about one thing. She hadn't trusted him—and perhaps that was part of the problem. Perhaps she should learn to be more like Jamie, simply accepting things as she found them? But then, he saw either the good or the bad. She saw all the bits in between. And what she felt for Martyn was far more complicated than Jamie's simple idolisation. . .

And this intense physical awareness between them was already beginning to get dangerously out of control. Martyn had said he wouldn't rush her into anything, and she respected him for that, at least, but she knew it would only take a look, a word from her and his self-control would be shattered. They both knew it was only a question of waiting for the right moment, and the physical intimacy they had once shared would be resumed, because it was becoming increasingly difficult for either of them to control the intense longing, the burning need for physical contact that made them want to be with each other, to touch each other in any way, no matter how trivial. . . But there was still the question of Martyn's divorce, and, on her side, there was still David.

Helen sighed heavily and let her eyes wander round the crowded field—or at least, the part of the field she could see from her position behind the cake stall. David was here this afternoon. He had insisted on bringing her the short distance from the Lodge in his car, driving carefully while she sat in the back, balancing the cakes and strawberry gâteaus she made as her contribution to the supply on the stall. She could just see the car now, parked where he had left it on the top field which was used as a car park, and when the afternoon was over he would take her back in it. Jamie was going to Hall Farm with Peter and the Thompsons, but she and David would go back to the Lodge to have something to eat, before getting changed and coming back again for the dance this evening.

Among the crowd, a dark head caught her eye, and she turned her head to see Martyn standing with Mrs

Edgeworth and two of the other committee members.
He was looking in her direction, and she could tell
from the look in his eyes that he'd seen her. She smiled
at him. His eyes moved down over the pink sun-dress,
then back up to her face, and suddenly, despite half
the field and Mrs Edgeworth between them, it was as
though they were the only two people in the world.
Then Helen's attention was distracted by a customer,
and when she looked up again Martyn had disappeared
into the show tent.

The cake stall was popular among the helpers who
served on the stalls on carnival day because unlike the
refreshments, or the children's sideshows, once all the
cakes had been sold and the money counted and
handed in, whoever helped on it was free to wander
off and enjoy themselves, and that was exactly what
Helen did. She bought herself an ice-cream and wandered across to the other side of the field, hoping to
see Jamie run the last of his races. But by the time she
got there the children's races had already finished, and
Jamie came running across, red-faced and out of
breath, to proudly show her his prize money.

'I won two races, but Peter beat me in the sack
race!' he complained, and Helen smiled.

'You wouldn't enter the races at all if it wasn't for
the prize money,' she teased him, and he gave a
sheepish grin.

'Can I go and spend some of it on the sideshows
now?' he pleaded, and with a warning not to spend it
all at once, she let him go.

'Oh, and by the way, Mum, Peter's mum wants to
see you,' Jamie called back over his shoulder. 'She's
over there somewhere. . .'

Helen's smile faded, and even as she turned to look

in the direction Jamie had pointed, she saw Liz waving to her from the other side of the running-track.

What on earth could Liz want to see her about? Unless it was that embarrassing incident on Monday night, when she'd interrupted her and Martyn?

But Liz was all smiles as she approached. 'Helen, I wanted to see you to say thank you for getting me that job up at the Folly,' she began breathlessly, almost as soon as she reached her. 'It's marvellous working for Mr Sayton—and I love cooking, you know!'

'I didn't get you the job, Liz,' Helen answered, surprised.

'Perhaps not, but you mentioned my name to Mr Sayton, and I'm really grateful. It's just what I need, and even though it's only temporary——'

'Temporary?' Helen's eyes had jerked back to Liz's face. 'Why? Is Martyn going back to London?' she demanded, feeling suddenly cold inside.

'Oh, no! At least, I don't think so——' Liz stammered, obviously surprised and taken aback by the sudden question. 'It's just that—well, he doesn't want to take on any permanent staff until he's decided what to do about the house—not that I think he'll sell it!' she added quickly. 'I know he's already contacted a couple of firms about estimates.'

'I see.' Helen was relaxing again, already ashamed of herself, of the sudden suspicion. These last couple of evenings she and Martyn had been round the rest of the downstairs rooms making notes, and he'd already told her he'd been in touch with one of the local contractors about the roof. But Liz was still watching her intently.

'Helen,' she began, 'why didn't you tell me you already knew Martyn—Mr Sayton? It was a surprise to us all.'

'I haven't been able to speak to you, Liz,' Helen pointed out. 'Not since that morning I went to the solicitors.'

'No—no, of course not,' Liz answered thoughtfully. 'It must have been a surprise to you, too, when he arrived instead of his father—a pleasant surprise, though,' she added, smiling. And then, 'I think it's all very romantic!'

Helen's eyebrows rose. 'You think it's romantic that Jamie and I might have to leave the Lodge?'

'Oh, that's been some kind of solicitor's error,' Liz dismissed with an airy wave of her hand. 'Mr Sayton wouldn't do anything as drastic as that—not to you, anyway,' she added, smiling even more. 'He'll look after you, Helen, I'm sure he will, and everything will work out. You'll see.'

She sounded just like Mrs Edgeworth, Helen thought to herself. Did the whole village think like this? But she merely shrugged noncommittally and said evasively, 'Perhaps,' then effectively changed the subject by asking, 'How come you're not helping on a stall this year?' And now it was Liz's turn to shrug.

'Mrs Edgeworth came to see me the other day, but I told her I was too busy now that I'm cooking for Mr Sayton—I've hardly seen the children this week!' she exclaimed. 'Bob's mother looks after them while I'm working, and Bob takes them to and from school and playgroup.' She turned to smile happily at her husband, who was just coming to join them from the direction of the children's amusements, two sticky twins in tow, and Helen saw the smile he gave her back.

'It looks as if everything's working out for you too,' she said, grinning at Liz, and Liz laughed, almost in surprise.

'Yes, it does, doesn't it?' She grinned, and slipped her hand into her husband's as they wandered away.

They'd only just disappeared into the crowd when Helen saw David coming towards her from the other direction. Smiling, she turned to greet him, but her heart sank at the look on his face.

'I've been looking for you everywhere, Helen!' he told her irritably. 'Why didn't you come to find me?'

'I've only just finished on the cake stall,' she pointed out. 'And I wanted to see Jamie race, but I was too late.'

'Well, we've found each other now,' he muttered. 'Do you want an ice-cream?'

It was his way of apologising, Helen realised, but she had to shake her head. 'I've just had one,' she admitted, and once again her heart sank as he scowled at his watch. 'It's nearly time for the prizes to be announced in the big marquee,' he muttered tersely. 'Shall we go?'

The show tent was crowded. The exhibits were laid out on long trestle tables that ran the length of the marquee, while at one end a large crowd had gathered round the small dais on which the committee chairman had just introduced Martyn, to a round of polite applause. Helen and David managed to squeeze just inside the entrance, but short of pushing her way through the crowd to the home-made section, there was no way Helen could find out if Sarah's jam had won a prize this year or not.

'Haven't you entered a flower arrangement this year?' David's voice came in her ear, and she nodded. Early this morning, in a fit of enthusiasm, she had picked some flowers from the garden and made them up into a simple arrangement, but she hardly expected to win anything with that. Kingsleigh Flower Club, of which Sarah had been a member a few years ago, usually carried off most of the prizes in that section——

Her thoughts were suddenly interrupted by the mention of her mother's name, and the next moment she felt David's hand in her back, pushing her forward.

'Sarah's jam has won again,' he muttered, and she stumbled forward through the crowd and up on to the dais. Martyn's hand clasped hers as he handed her the simple certificate, and she looked up into his eyes.

'This is for Sarah,' he said softly, and suddenly her eyes were full of tears. She swallowed painfully, only just managing to mumble a brief 'thank you' before she stepped down off the dais again. It was too much to push her way back to David, so she stayed where she was, the certificate clasped in trembling fingers while she struggled to control the sudden flood of emotion. Someone she knew patted her comfortingly on the shoulder and she managed a grateful smile, then she was composed again, clapping along with everyone else at the succession of prizewinners.

By the time the floral section came round, people were beginning to shift uncomfortably. It was hot in the marquee and everyone was crushed together, but the next minute Helen's head jerked up as she heard her own name announced, and she stepped up on to the dais again in dazed surprise. Her arrangement had won a prize! Once again Martyn's hand clasped hers and he grinned down at her.

'This is for you, Helen,' he murmured, and suddenly his mouth was on hers in a firm, hard kiss.

There was a sudden round of wolf-whistles and furious applause, and Helen felt the red heat of embarrassment sweep up her face.

'Was that necessary?' she got out through her teeth.

'I thought it was *very* necessary,' he said with a grin, under cover of the noise. 'Anyhow, it'll give everyone something to talk about, won't it?' and, with bland politeness, he shook her hand and handed her her certificate.

Once again she only just managed a brief 'thank you' before she stepped down again to more hearty claps on the shoulder, then suddenly David was at her side, his face indicative of his feelings.

'The swine!' he muttered furiously. 'That was completely unnecessary!' But Helen had caught sight of Liz, winking at her from the other side of the dais, and she pulled out her handkerchief and buried her face in it so that David wouldn't see her burst into a fit of uncontrollable giggles.

The journey home was completed in almost total silence. Helen gazed out of the window while David glared rigidly ahead, taking his fury out on the gears as they turned in through the Folly gates. The time had come, she realised hollowly. The situation was becoming intolerable for both of them—and surely now even David could see that there could be nothing between them. At least, not on her side.

She unlocked the kitchen door. Rags's tail thumped a greeting on the floor from where he lay in his bed in the corner, but for once she ignored him and walked straight through to the sitting-room, turning to face David as he hovered on the threshold. 'David——' she began hesitantly, but he put his hand up, silencing her.

'No, Helen, I know what you're going to say—but there's no need.' His voice sounded almost weary now. 'I can't fool myself any longer. It's over, isn't it?'

The look on his face filled her with nothing but sadness. 'It had hardly begun,' she told him gently.

'David, I tried to tell you that day you asked me to marry you——'

'I realise that now,' he sighed, and his mouth twisted into a smile. 'It was my own foolish pride that made me believe there could be anything more than friendship between us, and now I've ruined everything! I thought that all you needed was time, but I can see now that that was just a vain hope. I think that was why I proposed—as a last desperate effort, but all it did was complicate matters between us!'

'We were friends once,' Helen told him softly. 'Why can't we go back to being friends again?'

'Just friends?'

'Just friends, David.' She smiled. 'No strings on either side.'

'Agreed.' He smiled then too, and came forward to take her hand.

'Do you still want to take me to the dance this evening?' she questioned softly. 'I know we were supposed to be meeting Liz and her husband, but if you'd rather not——?'

But he shook his head. 'If you still want to go, Helen, then I'll take you,' he said, and his mouth twisted wryly. 'It'll be a special occasion after all, won't it?'

'In that case, I'll go and get us something to eat.' She smiled, and squeezed his hand.

They ate sandwiches in front of the television. David had brought wine, and she'd saved one of the strawberry gâteaus for afters, and by the time they had finished David was smiling again. He carried the plates through to the kitchen and Helen went up to get changed, feeling happily relieved that he was being so reasonable. She liked David. She liked him as a friend—and now, at least, she could talk to Martyn about him with a clear conscience. . .

She was putting the finishing touches to her make-up when there was the sound of a car outside, and the next moment she heard voices downstairs. First a man's voice, deep and unfamiliar, and then the lighter tones of a woman.

She went across to the window to see a silver-grey Mercedes parked in the drive and, curious now, she went to the top of the stairs.

A woman stood at the bottom, with her back to her, but the sight of that gleaming, expertly styled dark hair and the elegant figure below it made Helen freeze in shock.

Her knuckles were white on the banister rail as she started down the stairs, and the woman turned, looking up at her.

Helen reached the bottom step. She was vaguely aware of David coming to her side, Sarah's apron round his middle, and the tea-towel hanging limply from his arm.

'Helen——' he began, and his voice sounded strange. 'Helen, this is—is——'

'Martyn's wife,' Helen finished for him. 'I know.'

CHAPTER NINE

THE face hadn't changed. A little older perhaps, a little more self-assured, but that was only to be expected.

'Hello, Helen.'

The voice hadn't changed either, Helen realised in that first instant. It was like the smile, slow and cool. A slim hand was extended towards her and her own went out to meet it, her fingers sliding away from those cold, crimson-tipped ones almost as soon as they made contact.

'I'm surprised you remember me,' Jacqueline Beauford remarked, with that same cool smile, and Helen's eyebrows rose. How could she forget? That moment when she had finally met Martyn's father, when he had calmly introduced her to this elegant stranger, had lived with her every moment of the last nine years. She could even remember the feelings: the tortuous emotion, the shock. . .

She stared rigidly at Jacqueline. No, nothing had changed, she thought. It had been a foolish illusion on her part that these last few days she had almost managed to blank it out, to forget it. After all, hadn't Martyn always led a strange kind of double life? One life in London and the other here, at Sayton's Folly? And when he had explained what had happened nine years ago hadn't she accepted it almost without question, in the willing belief that he was proving to her that he could be trusted after all?

But now, it seemed, that too had been a foolish

illusion on her part. He had said his life in London was over, but how could it be, when Jacqueline Beauford was here, living proof that she still played some part in his life?

'Is Martyn expecting you?' Helen asked now, and was surprised to discover how calm her own voice sounded in comparison to the turmoil inside her, and she gave a brief thought to what Martyn's reaction would be when he knew that Jacqueline was here—or was he going to say that this too was a trick of his father's that he knew nothing about?

'Martyn wanted some papers from London,' Jacqueline explained airily. 'So I thought I'd surprise him and bring them down myself. Unfortunately, we got lost.' She waved a hand at her companion. 'These country lanes tend to look all the same after a while, don't they?' And as she calmly walked through into the sitting-room they all, perforce, had to follow. 'This, by the way, is Martyn's agent, Charles Hughes,' she added, almost as an afterthought, and once again waved an airy hand, this time dismissively, towards her companion.

He was older, tall and grey-haired, but still very distinguished-looking, and his eyes smiled warmly at Helen as he took her hand to shake it firmly.

'We saw this charming little place and decided to stop and ask directions,' Jacqueline continued from where she had taken up position on the hearthrug. 'And your—er—husband, Helen, told us we'd found the place after all!'

Her eyes had been wandering inquisitively round the room, but on the last sentence they came to rest penetratingly on David.

'David isn't my husband.'

Jacqueline's eyes swivelled back to Helen, and her eyebrows rose enquiringly. 'Oh. Isn't he?'

Helen ignored the implication and retorted coolly. 'He's a friend. David Evans, this is Jacqueline——'

'Jacqueline Beauford Sayton,' Jacqueline smoothly interrupted the introduction, and it was all Helen could do then to keep the mask of her face in place. Jacqueline's deliberate use of the Sayton name had sent a pain like a knife through her heart, but Jacqueline seemed completely unaware of her set features as David's proffered hand was ignored and her eyes went back to her surroundings.

'What a charming room,' she remarked airily. 'I suppose most of this furniture is your mother's, Helen?'

Helen's eyes jerked back to Jacqueline. How did Jacqueline know about Sarah—*what* did she know about Sarah? But Jacqueline was already continuing, 'And your son? Where is he at the moment?'

And now Helen was rigid. Jacqueline knew about *Jamie*? 'He—he's staying at a friend's house,' she got out after a moment.

'Oh, really? He must be getting quite old now—let me see. Six? Seven?'

'Eight,' Helen supplied tonelessly.

'Oh, yes, of course! How silly of me—and I can even remember your husband now. Simon, wasn't it?' Jacqueline gave a little sigh. 'Such a pity that he should leave you all alone like this. . .' There was just the right amount of sadness in her voice. 'But then, you still have your son, Helen.'

Something in that last sentence made Helen look up quickly, eyes narrowing on Jacqueline's serene features, but Jacqueline's dark eyes had already moved back to Charles Hughes.

'Well, I suppose we'd better be on our way. . .'

Almost on cue, he nodded and took Helen's hand again with gentlemanly courtesy, but Jacqueline brushed past them on her way to the door.

'Do get a move on, Charles,' she ordered briskly, and the next moment they had gone.

David followed them to the door, but Helen stayed where she was in the middle of the room, her face frozen. She heard the car start up and purr away, and then the door close and David's footsteps coming back down the hall.

He stood in the doorway for a moment, staring at her, his face full of compassion; but this time, when he would have spoken, it was Helen who put up her hand for silence.

'David, I don't think I want to go to the dance after all. . .'

Helen vaguely recognised the sound of a car. There was a screech of brakes, the slam of a car door, and the next moment someone was banging on the front door.

She was still where David had left her, sitting on the hearthrug, her arms hugging her knees, and when the banging came again she frowned and lifted her head to look at the clock on the mantelpiece. Ten-thirty—is that all? she thought wearily, and climbed stiffly to her feet.

She opened the door to find Martyn standing there, his hand already raised to knock again, and in one glance he had taken in her tousled hair and the crumpled silk of her dress.

'Why aren't you at the dance?' he demanded harshly, and then he was brushing past her, striding through to the sitting-room to flick the lamp on and stare round with narrowed eyes. 'Where's Evans?' he demanded tautly.

'I sent him away.'

He turned back to her then, noticing, as if for the first time, how pale she was, her untouched lipstick, her bare feet. 'What do you mean—you sent him away?' he questioned sharply, but she walked past him to flop into the armchair.

'Why are you here?' she asked tonelessly.

He straightened, but his eyes were still fixed on her in that same narrowed stare. 'I've been down to the village—to the dance. Good lord, the place is bursting at the seams! It took me nearly an hour to realise you weren't there—nor Evans either. Even Liz Thompson and her husband were getting worried. . .' He paused, still watching her. 'Helen, what's wrong? Are you ill?'

'No.'

'Then why are you sitting here all alone in the dark?'

'I didn't want to go to the dance.'

'I would have thought that was obvious!' Despite the sarcasm, his voice had softened, then suddenly his face changed. 'Helen, Evans didn't—*try* anything, did he?'

She looked up at him then, a look almost of disgust. 'My goodness, that's rich!' she snapped. 'Coming from you—when your *wife* is up at the Folly!' And she flung herself out of the armchair to pace away from him across the rug.

He stiffened. 'You've seen Jackie?'

'Oh, yes, I've seen her!' she burst out. 'She made sure of that!' And she turned back to him, then, her eyes brilliant with unshed tears. 'She called here to ask for directions—can you imagine? I'm surprised you didn't supply her with a printed guide while you were at it!'

'You think I sent for her?' he asked incredulously.

'Why else would she be here?' She swung away from him to rake unsteady fingers through her hair. 'For heaven's sake, Martyn, you told me your life in London was over!'

'It is!'

'Then why is Jacqueline here?' she demanded, and now it was almost impossible to keep the tremor out of her voice.

'Helen!' He made to come towards her, but she stepped back, keeping the armchair between them, and he checked himself, drawing a harsh breath before beginning again, 'Helen, believe me, it was as big a shock for me as it was for you! If I'd known Charles would bring her——'

'But Charles *did* bring her—and why would he unless you asked him to?' Helen accused in a brittle voice. 'After all, you're supposed to be divorcing her, aren't you? Or was that just a line so that you could string *me* along?'

'You know damn well I'm divorcing her!' Martyn declared tautly. 'I've already told you——'

'Oh, yes, I forgot,' she interrupted caustically, 'you only married her because I married Simon—isn't that what you said?' She gave a bitter smile. 'Tell me, Martyn, what was that you said about no more deception—or was that, too, all part of the plan? So that you could bring *Mrs Sayton* to Sayton's Folly and prove to the whole of Penford that you can keep two women going at the same time after all?'

His jaw had hardened furiously. 'Good grief, Helen, you think that's all you mean to me—an affair?'

'I don't know what to think!' she choked unsteadily. 'But it's obvious that Jacqueline knows what's been going on here! She knew all about my mother—and

Simon and Jamie—and who else could have told her but *you*?'

Martyn was staring at her incredulously, his face pale in the lamplight, hard and set. 'Jackie *knows*?'

'I could hardly believe it!' Helen got out. 'Not of *you*, Martyn—but then, I could hardly believe it nine years ago either!' she added with bitter pain. 'It was only when I went down to London that day, and your father explained to me why you hadn't returned to Sayton's Folly. He told me all about your commitments in London—he even introduced me to one! Jacqueline Beauford, the girl you were engaged to marry!'

'Good lord, but I wasn't——' His body was rigid now, and even in the lamplight she could see the way his eyes glittered with suppressed fury. 'So that's what he told you!'

Helen closed her eyes for a moment against the tears that were threatening. 'Do you think that hasn't haunted me, Martyn? Haunted me for the last nine years?'

'Simon knew too, didn't he?' he demanded in that same incredulous tone. 'Tell me, Helen, is that what you meant about his protecting you—why you married him so soon after? Because you thought I was going to marry Jackie?'

'But you did marry her, didn't you?' she accused, and now she could hardly see him for the tears in her eyes.

'Oh, yes, I married her then,' he ground out, 'and it was the biggest mistake I ever made in my life!'

'That's easy for you to say now!'

His eyes jerked back to her face. 'You're saying you don't believe me—after everything that's happened between us?'

'The same thing happened nine years ago, Martyn!' she got out. 'We were lovers then! And all the while you were here, with me, Jacqueline was tucked away in London, waiting for you!'

'There was *nothing* between me and Jackie nine years ago!' he muttered forcibly.

She swallowed painfully. 'You expect me to believe that?'

'It's the truth!' he declared tautly. 'And you can believe what I told you the other day too!'

'You—you expect me to believe that your father would tell me a deliberate lie?' she got out in a choked whisper.

'He would have done anything, Helen!' Martyn declared harshly. 'Anything to bring me back to London and keep me there—away from Sayton's Folly! You see, by then he'd realised that I had no intention of joining the firm, that I had gone abroad to paint—and he must have known, too, that I had some crazy idea of asking you to join me!'

'*Me?*' She stared at him with wide, tear-stained eyes, and with a harsh sigh he swung away from her to pace restlessly across the carpet.

'Why do you think I went to stay with those friends of mine?' His voice was almost a groan now. 'I had to think, Helen! To try and sort out some kind of future—for both of us! I wanted to take you with me, yes, but you already had a place at university. It would have meant asking you to give that up, to give up any chance of a career for yourself—and I wasn't even sure I could support myself, let alone you as well—as my father so realistically pointed out!'

'He—he knew about me?'

'Oh, yes, he knew!' he retorted bitterly. 'Don't ask me how—but he did!'

'And—and he told me you were going to marry Jacqueline—because of *us*?' she questioned incredulously.

'There was more to it than that,' he admitted harshly. 'You see, Jackie's father was the other major shareholder in the firm, and our families had always been keen for us to marry—not because we were passionately in love,' he derided bitterly, 'but because my father was determined that the firm should continue in the Sayton line—and marrying me off to Jackie was his way of achieving it! He told me at my brother's funeral that it was time I settled down to join the firm—and marry Jackie. Of course I told him to go to hell—on both counts!' He ran angry fingers through his hair. 'No doubt he thought he'd really hit the jackpot that day you went down to London—good lord, Helen, I can see it all now!'

'But—but what about Jacqueline?' Helen whispered tautly. 'She was so convincing that day, so—so *confident*!'

'I'll bet she was!' he muttered through his teeth. 'She always did have an eye to the main chance. She was just like my father, Helen, ruthless and ambitious! My father may have wanted an heir to inherit the firm—but she wanted the Sayton name just as badly— and she made sure I knew it!'

'And—and that was all there was between you then—the firm?'

'What else could there be, when I thought you were here at Sayton's Folly—waiting for me?'

She was silent for a moment, staring at him, then she whispered unsteadily, 'You should have asked me to go with you, Martyn. You should at least have given me the choice.'

'Well, as it happened, I didn't get the chance, did

I?' he muttered harshly, and came to stand in front of her again then, his eyes fixed on her face, dark and intense. 'You should have waited, Helen,' he murmured abruptly. 'I can hardly believe you fell for my father's tricks so easily—and to marry Simon so soon after——!'

'But you married Jacqueline in the end, didn't you?' she contradicted unevenly.

'Oh, yes, I was so devastated, I lost my nerve and bowed to pressure—and you can see how it's turned out!'

'Even so, Jacqueline's here—at Sayton's Folly.'

'But I had no idea she was coming, believe me!' His voice was hardening again. 'Why do you think I arrived the way I did that night, wanting no one to know I was here? Jackie knew about Gerald—about Sayton's Folly. I knew that as soon as she realised I was back in the country, she'd be down here like a shot to see my inheritance for herself, to see how much it was worth in the way of a divorce settlement—and I was right!' he added with bitter sarcasm. 'Somehow she'd discovered that I'd been in touch with Charles, and apparently she damn near forced him into giving her a lift down here! But as to how she knew about you and Jamie——' a muscle jerked in his jaw '—I've no idea, Helen, but I'll find out, believe me!'

'I realised you were bitter about the divorce,' she said slowly, staring down at her fingers as they traced the pattern of the armchair, 'but I thought—I thought it was because you still cared for her.'

'You were jealous.'

Her eyes came back to his, and his mouth twisted into a crooked little smile. 'It's an emotion I know something about, Helen,' he confessed with wry self-derision, and his hand came out to hers then, his fingers entwining with hers, drawing her towards him. 'How do you think I felt when I heard about you and Simon? How do you think I felt tonight when I found you sitting in the dark?' His fingers gently stroked the trace of tears from her cheek. 'I think it's time you did some explaining of your own. What did you mean when you said you'd sent David Evans away?'

'Oh, Martyn, you've no need to be jealous of David!' she exclaimed, and something in his eyes sent a tremor of emotion through her. 'I've told you, he's just a friend.'

His hands slid up her arms, holding her in front of him and only slightly away from him as his eyes looked into hers, dark and deeply disturbing. 'I thought that about Simon once.'

'David isn't quite in Simon's league,' she breathed unsteadily, 'or yours either—oh, Martyn, I've been such a fool!' She leant against him then, letting her head fall forward on to his shoulder. 'If I hadn't been so ready to believe what your father told me that day——'

His fingers were in her hair, stroking, caressing. 'Didn't I warn you about him often enough?' he muttered tautly. 'But no doubt Gerald too wasn't slow in giving you *his* opinion of me!'

She sighed then. 'Gerald never said anything against you.'

'Oh, no?' he muttered caustically. 'He simply condoned what my father said by his silence!'

'You should have told me about Jacqueline,' she sighed. 'I would have understood.'

'Would you?' He pulled her head back then to look into her eyes. 'You were so young, Helen. How did I know it wouldn't have made you unsure, suspicious, as I was about Simon?'

'You didn't,' she breathed, 'but you should have trusted me.'

'We should have trusted each other,' he told her tautly, then his voice deepened. 'But that's all in the past now, Helen, our past—and at least Jackie's appearance here this weekend hasn't been completely wasted.'

Her eyes widened, and once again his mouth twisted. 'At least I know now that you don't still hate me,' he continued, his voice husky now. 'If you can be jealous of Jackie like that, then you must still care for me a little.'

She half smiled. 'Only a little? Oh, Martyn, I——'

She stopped, but he urged, breathlessly gentle now, 'Say it, Helen. Tell me how you feel—let me hear you say it!'

She smiled then, her eyes as warm and inviting as a summer sea. She brushed her mouth across his in a sensuous caress. 'I love you,' she breathed against his lips.

He was suddenly still. '*My darling!*' he whispered hoarsely, then she was crushed against him as his mouth hardened into a fierce, possessive kiss, and she abandoned herself to it, sliding her arms round his neck and pressing herself against him, feeling a familiar fire beginning deep inside her even as she felt his body hardening against hers; but there was no drawing back, no hesitation this time. Now, at last, she was ready to be part of him again, not just to take what he had to offer, but to unite with him and feel again that ecstasy that had been so long denied.

He bore her down on to the sofa. His kisses were heated, full of smouldering intensity, and with an impatient groan his jacket and tie were discarded. Even his shirt seemed an unbearable barrier between them now, and her fingers fumbled with the buttons, and the next moment she was sliding her palms up his back, feeling the thrill of bare skin—and his quickened heartbeat—with a whisper of satisfaction; but then the breath caught in her throat. The low-cut bodice of her dress was off her shoulders, and his mouth had found the smooth, tantalisingly pale skin of her breasts, and two rosy peaks, already dark and swollen with desire.

'Good lord, Helen,' he breathed raggedly, staring down at her with eyes that seemed to burn wherever they touched. 'I came out tonight with the hope of nothing more than a couple of dances with you—and now there's only one thought in my head. . .' His lips came back to brush hers in a brief, aching caress, as he whispered hoarsely '. . .to make love to you!'

'Then why don't you?' she breathed against his neck. 'There's nothing to stop us now, Martyn! Don't say no this time—stay with me here, tonight——' and she trailed her fingers down the soft, curling hairs of his chest.

With a ragged breath he caught her hand, carrying her fingers to his lips to kiss them one by one. 'Yes,' he whispered. 'Yes—*yes*! Oh, Helen, if you knew how I've longed to hear you say that! I'll stay with you, my darling girl,' he breathed unsteadily, 'but not like this. Not here on your mother's sofa! That's all in the past, Helen. We have nothing to hide—and there'll be no subterfuge, no shadows from the past to spoil our happiness this time. When I make you mine I want the whole of Penford to know about it—the whole world! Besides,' he added with a shaky smile, 'there's something I want to show you up at the Folly. A surprise. . .' There was a wealth of promise in his voice, and his eyes were dark and heavy with passion.

She looked up at him from under her lashes. 'You

wicked man—not your *etchings* again?' she teased
softly, and her fingers caressed the sensitive skin of his
navel.

'You little witch!' In one quick movement he had
caught her hand and twisted his body so that she was
almost lying on top of him, and he pulled her against
him to give her a fierce, hard kiss. 'What else could it
be *except* my etchings?' he growled, and she giggled,
then her eyes widened as she saw the laughter in his
eyes.

'The portrait of Jamie!' she exclaimed in excitement.
'You've finished it?'

'Didn't I tell you it was nearly finished?' He grinned,
and she raised herself on her elbows to bestow a last
passionate kiss on his parted lips.

'Then what are we waiting for?' she murmured
huskily. 'Let's go!' And, smilingly, she disentangled
herself to re-do the buttons on his shirt.

They drove up to the Folly in the Porsche, her hand
on his knee, his eyes stealing back to glance at her
face. The house was in darkness, and he held her close
as he led her across the tiled hall, planting a swift kiss
on her upturned mouth as he opened the conservatory
door. The central light blazed into life—and Helen
gasped in amazement.

The portrait was still on its easel, but uncovered
now, facing the door in silent splendour, almost as
though it had been waiting for her. She approached it
slowly.

It was Jamie all right—every line of his face, every
detail—with Rags at his feet. He sat at the base of a
tree, surrounded by the soft, sunlit green of bracken
and the rich browns of crackling twigs—exactly as she
remembered him from that day at Delamere.

'It's beautiful!' Emotion put a catch in her voice,

and she turned back to Martyn, feeling the prick of tears behind her eyelids.

He came to her then, holding her hand as he stood next to her, surveying the portrait. 'It's one of the best things I've done. Charles is furious.'

'Furious?' she echoed dazedly. 'But why?'

'I've told him he can use it for the exhibition, but it's not for sale.' His eyes had moved to her face. 'I've decided to keep it, to hang it here, at Sayton's Folly.'

'Oh, Martyn, *that's wonderful*!'

'Yes, it is, isn't it? but I wonder if he knows exactly what he's letting himself in for?'

The voice from the doorway made them both turn. Jacqueline stood there, a glass in one hand, a half-smoked cigarette in the other, her eyes moving speculatively from one to the other of them. 'Darling, you didn't tell me we were expecting—*visitors*,' she drawled, with that slow smile, and Helen felt her own smile freeze on her lips.

'You told me you had a headache. I thought you'd be in bed by now,' Martyn declared, and his voice too seemed suddenly cooler.

'What, without you to tuck me in?' Jacqueline retorted sweetly. 'Anyway, I knew when you went out that you wouldn't be long—I never realised before what a short distance it is to the bottom of the drive!'

Helen felt Martyn stiffen at her side. 'You've already said what you came up here to say, Jackie, and I've given you my answer!' he countered coldly. 'Now leave Helen out of this.'

'Oh, but I can't, Martyn! She's already a part of it— and she has been for the last nine years, haven't you, Helen?' There was a gleam, almost of amusement, in Jacqueline's eyes now as they switched to Helen's startled features. 'And anyway, surely you've told her,

Martyn? Surely you've told her the *real* reason why I'm here this weekend—to talk about a *reconciliation*?' Her smile turned to a derisive sneer. 'Oh, dear, I can see from Helen's face that you haven't! And I can see now too that you were hoping to keep me out of it— well, no matter.' She shrugged. 'I can be patient. I can see what a cosy family group you make—the three of you—*together*.' Her eyes had moved from Martyn's furious features, to Helen, to the portrait, inspecting each face in turn. 'The boy makes a very good subject, doesn't he?' she questioned sweetly. 'But then, you always were good with children, weren't you, Martyn?'

'The portrait is nothing to do with you, and you know it!' Martyn ground out. 'And neither is Jamie.'

Jacqueline gave a tinkling laugh. 'Oh, but he's *everything* to do with me—and he's everything to do with you too, Martyn, only you don't realise it yet!' and once again she smiled that sweet, sickly smile. 'I don't suppose you've told Helen that I still share the London house?' she added coyly.

Martyn's eyes had narrowed dangerously. '*Jackie!*' But Jacqueline was already advancing towards the portrait.

'Your son obviously takes after your side of the family, Helen,' she threw over her shoulder. 'Just as well, really,' she added, and Helen stood rigidly at Martyn's side, her hand no longer holding his, but clenched convulsively at her side.

'I—I'm not sure I take your meaning. . .' She was remembering Jacqueline's visit to the Lodge earlier, the emphasis in her voice, the questions she had asked about Jamie—and icy fingers were running up and down her spine.

Surely Jacqueline couldn't *know*?

'I always remember that day you came to see

Martyn's father,' Jacqueline continued, a curious little smile at the corners of her mouth as she turned to face her. 'I always remember thinking how—*desperate* you looked, Helen.'

'I'm not surprised she was desperate!' Martyn exploded furiously. 'Good grief, Jackie, when I think of what you did that day——!'

'Oh, but I wasn't the only one,' Jacqueline retorted slyly. 'Helen played her part too!' Her eyes were fixed on Helen, and there was nothing Helen could do but stare helplessly back as slowly, deliberately, Jacqueline turned to Martyn.

'I'm surprised she never told you,' she drawled sweetly. 'I certainly would have—but then, I'm not her! I realised as soon as I saw her that day that she was pregnant!'

CHAPTER TEN

IT SEEMED to Helen that the whole world had suddenly ground to a halt. She was vaguely aware of Jacqueline's triumphant, self-satisfied smile, and then Martyn advancing on her, his face livid, contorted with anger.

'You lying little bitch! Helen told me exactly what happened nine years ago—and she wasn't even married to Simon that day she went down to London!'

'You fool!' Jacqueline snapped at him. 'You don't need to be married to be pregnant!' she derided angrily. 'Are you so besotted that you can't work things out for yourself? I'm not talking about him—I'm talking about *you*!' Her voice had become a taunting, derisive purr. 'Have you never asked yourself why she was so desperate to see you? Why don't you ask her how old the boy is—*exactly* how old he is?'

Martyn seemed suddenly frozen. His eyes were fixed on Jacqueline in a fierce, malevolent glare and his breathing seemed shallow and uneven. '*Get out!*' he ground out through his teeth. 'Get out of here before I break your bloody neck!'

Jacqueline's smug triumph had returned in full force. 'Tut, tut, darling,' she murmured sweetly, 'there's no point in being cross with *me*!' Her malicious smile flicked over Helen as she sauntered to the door, then she added coyly to Martyn, 'Anyway, who knows, you might even thank me for it later. . .!' and the door closed behind her.

In the silence that followed, Jacqueline's heels could be heard tap-tapping away across the hall, and slowly

Martyn turned to face Helen. He stared at her for a moment, then moved, almost like an automaton, to stand in front of the portrait, staring at it with narrowed, penetrating eyes. Then slowly he turned back to Helen again, and her heart seemed to shrivel and die inside her.

'Well?' he demanded. 'Aren't you at least going to tell me that Jackie has got her dates wrong—that it's all a mistake?'

Her tongue seemed stuck to the roof of her mouth, and her voice, when it came, was nothing more than a strained whisper. '*Martyn, believe me, I never wanted you to find out like this*——'

He stared at her, and a look almost of disbelief passed over his face. '*For pity's sake!*' he exploded suddenly. 'I've spent the last couple of weeks trying to come to terms with my feelings for the boy—the boy I thought was Simon's son—only to discover——!' He couldn't finish. His eyes narrowed on her again, and now they were burning with a fierce, furious flame. 'Tell me, Helen, would you *ever* have told me?' he demanded tautly. 'Or were you going to let me play at being a father for a while until you decided whether or not I *deserved* to know?'

'I would have told you,' she began desperately. 'But——'

'You *would* have told me?' he bit out. 'Didn't you think I had a *right* to know I had a son?'

'I *tried* to tell you!' she exclaimed, her voice rising in intensity now. 'Why do you think I went down to London to try and see you? But you know what happened that day! For heaven's sake, do you think I wasn't *desperate*?'

'Is that why you decided to pay me back by keeping my son a secret from me?' he snapped, and his face was rigid and dark with anger. 'Tell me, Helen,' he demanded furiously, 'does it make you feel any better that you've deprived me of the first eight years of my son's life?'

She couldn't answer then, couldn't even face him, and she turned to stare desolately through the glass of the conservatory. The trees were silhouetted against the night sky, while above them the moon was rising, pale and clear.

'You said I should have waited,' she got out in a taut whisper. 'But you can see now that I couldn't, Martyn, *I couldn't*!'

'Good grief, I've spent the last couple of days trying to fit the final pieces of the jigsaw together, trying to understand why you married Simon so soon after——' He stopped abruptly, then she heard the breath hiss from between his teeth as he demanded incredulously, 'Did Simon know about all this? Tell me, Helen did *he* know what he was letting himself in for?'

She hesitated. He had taken a step towards her, and now the dark outline of his reflection glared at her from the glass, the dark intensity of his eyes shutting out the trees, shutting out even the moon itself.

'He guessed right from the start,' she said at last. 'It was he who took me down to London that day.'

'And he was still willing to marry you—knowing you were carrying another man's child?'

'He loved me,' she managed. 'And I loved him. Oh, as you said, not in the way I loved you—but I cared for him, and I like to think that in the end I made him happy.'

'Then why didn't you give him a child, Helen?' he ground out. 'Why didn't you complete your little family by giving him a son too? After all, you had plenty of time!'

'I've told you, Martyn, my marriage to Simon is none of your business——!'

'You've made it my business, Helen!' he interrupted tautly. 'You made it my business the day you let Simon Ashley give my child his name!' And he came to her then, grasping her shoulders to force her round to face him, while his eyes bored into hers, dark and fiercely penetrating, willing her to answer. 'Tell me, Helen!' he demanded. 'I have a right to know—and there can be no secrets between us now, not after this!'

She swallowed painfully. 'I couldn't have a child—not with Simon.'

He frowned down at her. 'Why not? Simon may have suffered with his health for most of his life, but that didn't affect his ability to father a child—and I know he wanted children!'

'You don't understand!' Once again she hesitated, and a tear rolled silently down her cheek as she looked up at him. He was tearing her apart, destroying her as she had always known he could by demanding everything she had to give, and now her memories of those final, painful, bitter-sweet months with Simon were all she had left.

'In the beginning I was very ill,' she began unsteadily. 'I was in and out of hospital all the while I was pregnant—and it was a difficult birth. By the time I'd recovered Simon was already into his final illness, and though at first we didn't realise how serious it was, he'd already discovered that he couldn't—that he was unable to——'

She stopped, swallowing past the emotion that was threatening to engulf her, and Martyn stared at her, his face incredulous as his fingers finally slackened their painful grip on her shoulders.

'Good lord, you mean—the marriage was *unconsummated*?'

She nodded dumbly, closing her eyes for a moment against the tears that were overflowing. 'It was something Simon felt guilty about almost to the very end—but he needn't have done,' she whispered tautly, and raised her head then, staring up at him in tearful defiance. 'In every other respect he was as much a husband to me and a father to Jamie as any man could have been! He looked after us—he *cared* for us! He said no one would ever guess the truth—and they didn't! He loved Jamie as much as if he had been his. He *was* Jamie's father, Martyn, in every respect but one, and nothing you, or Jacqueline Beauford, or anyone else can say will ever take that away!'

And with that she jerked away from him and stumbled blindly to the door, across the hall and through the front door, to flee across the moonlit grass towards the trees.

She watched the sun come up with desolate, tear-stained eyes, but the golden rays slanting through her mother's bedroom window had no strength to warm her. She sat on the floor with her back against the bed, still fully dressed from last night, and she had already heard two cars roar down the drive and away into the distance—first the grey Mercedes, and then, a few moments later, the Porsche and the sound of its passing seemed to leave a great gaping emptiness in her heart.

Oh, lord, was it only two weeks ago that she had wanted to hear that sound—that she had *wanted* Martyn to leave?

Yesterday morning at this time she had been out in the garden cutting flowers. Everything had seemed so

simple—the way ahead had seemed so clear. She had
even begun to plan how she would tell Martyn about
Jamie, how she would break it to him about his son. . .
She drew a shuddering sigh.

She had always thought that when the danger came
it would come from village gossip, from a carelessly
spoken word that would finally enable Sarah to put
two and two together. She had never dreamed that it
would come from a woman she had met only briefly
nine years ago—Jacqueline Beauford! But it had
shocked her too, the way Martyn had taken the news,
the way he had accused her of deliberately keeping
Jamie a secret from him—was that some measure of
how much Jamie had come to mean to him these last
few days?

It was all she could do not to dial Liz at Hall Farm,
to check that Jamie was still there, safe and well. . .
Oh, lord! Hadn't she always known that something
like this would happen? Hadn't she always feared it?

But nothing in all her wildest imaginings had prepared her for the look on Martyn's face last night, the
anger, the hatred in his eyes when he'd looked at
her. . . She sighed again and her head fell back against
the coverlet as she stared bleakly up at the ceiling.

She had fled from the Folly, but for once she had
found no solace here, in this place she loved, and she
had paced distraughtly from room to room, until at
last she had come into her mother's room, the only
sanctuary she knew. She needed to think, to come to
some kind of decision, she realised dully, but what
that decision would be she hadn't a clue. Only one
thing was certain now. After the way Martyn had
looked at her last night, she couldn't stay here—and
now that he knew the truth about Jamie, did she want

to? Because it would mean living next door to him—perhaps seeing him every day—seeing him with Jamie——!

Could she bear seeing them together, knowing that she couldn't share in their happiness? Because if what Jacqueline had insinuated last night was true. . .!

With a harsh breath she raised her head again, and her eyes wandered blindly round the familiar room, picking up heartaching memories here and there. She hadn't been in here since Sarah's death—she hadn't been able to bring herself to come in, but the trauma of last night had overtaken everything else, including her grief, and now she stared mistily at Sarah's brush and comb on the dressing-table, the photograph of her father beside the bed, and Sarah's box on the chest of drawers.

She would have to go through Sarah's things, she thought desolately. She should have done it before, but it had been too soon then. But now she realised the whole room needed doing—the whole house! Because if they were going to leave, if *she* was going to leave. . .

She climbed stiffly to her feet to tuck the box under her arm and carry it carefully downstairs to the sitting-room.

It was inlaid wood, with a brass lock at the front, and Helen had pulled every drawer out of the bureau before she'd found the key. She put the box on the hearthrug and knelt in front of it.

Her father had brought it back from India years ago, and ever since his death it had been Sarah's box. She'd kept all her personal things in it, as well as family documents, birth certificates, important receipts. . .

Helen turned the key and gently lifted the lid. Her mother had never felt so close as she did now.

The box was full of papers, all neatly stacked and tied together in small bundles, except for one or two envelopes—one of them quite new-looking and covered with familiar, spidery writing—but she put these to one side as she caught sight of two photographs. One was of herself and her father—she could only have been about five when it had been taken—but the other one was of Jamie when he had been new-born.

She stared at it, and her throat closed up as love and despair welled up from deep inside, threatening to choke her, to break her heart in two. *Oh, lord. . .!*

'Helen?'

The voice from the doorway made her jump. She looked up. Martyn stood there, hands thrust into his pockets and the collar of his jacket turned up against the cool morning air, and for a moment she could only stare at him, shaken as much by his appearance as anything else. He looked terrible, but then, did she look any better? she thought distractedly. They must make a fine pair—both of them still in evening dress, hair ruffled and untidy, staring at each other with pale, drawn faces and red-rimmed eyes. Martyn had a shadow of dark growth along his jaw. He looked as though he hadn't slept all night—hadn't even been to bed—but then, had she? The photographs slid from her nerveless fingers.

'I thought you'd left,' she said unsteadily.

His eyes left hers to wander round the room, narrowing on the papers strewn everywhere, the drawers pulled out of the bureau—the general chaos. 'It looks as though you're just about to!' he muttered tautly.

'I'm sorting through my mother's things,' she returned in the same unsteady tone.

'Is Jamie still at Hall Farm?' It wasn't so much a

question, more a demand, and Helen got to her feet, facing him defiantly.

'What did you expect? That I'd spirit him away somewhere overnight simply to stop you—and your wife—from getting your hands on him?' she derided bitterly. Oh, *if only she could!*

'You couldn't take him anywhere—you have nowhere else to go!' Martyn began tightly. 'And besides, he's a Sayton. He belongs here, at Sayton's Folly—and while we're on the subject, I've spent the whole night going over those papers from London! For heaven's sake, Helen, why didn't you tell me that you'd written to the London solicitors—that your mother hadn't paid any rent for years?' he demanded harshly. 'No wonder Jackie told me I'd be better off selling the Lodge to her! But then, she never was short on business acumen; she always could turn a situation to her advantage. She worked something out in two minutes that it took me nine years to discover!'

Helen stared at him, hardly daring to believe what she had just heard. Jacqueline Beauford living *here*?

'Good grief, Martyn, you're just like the rest of your family after all!' she got out in a cracked whisper. 'It's all *possessions* with you, isn't it? You only came down to Sayton's Folly in the first place to see what you could get out of it in financial terms—and now you've discovered you have a claim on Jamie too! No wonder Jacqueline needs patience!' she exclaimed with a derisive twist of her mouth. 'Tell me, is that how you see me too? As some kind of possession that you can pick up and put down again whenever you feel like it?'

His features were already pale, but now they had tautened too. 'You're a fine one to talk about possessions, Helen! You've kept Jamie to yourself all these years——'

'And because of that, you think you can just walk in here and take him away from me?' she interrupted incredulously. 'Believe me, Martyn, I'll fight you tooth and nail for Jamie's happiness—and Jacqueline too, if necessary!' she declared fiercely. 'My goodness, you're as cold-blooded as she is—you deserve each other! The sooner I get Jamie away from here, the better!'

'So you are leaving?'

His face had hardened into a taut mask. Only his eyes were alive now, glittering at her from under fierce black brows.

She swallowed painfully. 'The six weeks will be up soon.'

'And that's your excuse for walking out of my life—like you did nine years ago?' he questioned harshly. 'You made a promise to me, Helen!'

She stared at him. 'What promise?'

'You promised me you'd stay at Sayton's Folly—at least until everything was sorted out.'

'It is sorted out—at least, as far as I'm concerned,' she choked, and flung herself down on to the sofa. 'And I don't need an excuse to leave, Martyn. You made your feelings about me very clear last night!'

He walked round to stand in front of her, staring down at her with hard, unreadable eyes. 'I was angry last night, Helen,' he told her tautly. 'Angry and shocked—because it was Jacqueline who told me about Jamie and not you! I was furious—and can you blame me? After all, as you so succinctly pointed out, I am a Sayton.' His mouth twisted then with a hint of wry humour, but she looked away, her eyes bleak.

'Now who's making excuses?'

'You told me you loved me, Helen. Last night—here on this very sofa. Didn't that mean anything either?' he demanded roughly.

'Of course it did—but then I didn't know why Jacqueline was here!'

'And you do now?'

'She wants you back—she made no secret of it!' she got out in a choked voice. 'And from what you just said about the Lodge, it sounds as though she's got what she wanted after all!'

'Oh, Jackie's got what she wanted,' Martyn retorted harshly, 'and much good may it do her! Why do you think she was in such a hurry to leave? She couldn't wait to get back to London!'

She lifted her head to stare at him. 'Jackie's left?'

His mouth twisted. 'Who do you think was driving the Mercedes hell for leather down the drive? Charles was furious! She didn't even ask—simply took his keys and drove off, so I let him borrow the Porsche to go after her and check that she didn't drive his car into a ditch or something!' He looked at his watch. 'They should be halfway to London by now.'

'But I thought—I thought it was *you* who'd left!' she stammered.

'Why would I leave when everything I want is here, at Sayton's Folly?' he asked, and suddenly there was a new note in his voice, a note that set her heart pounding, making it almost impossible to breathe. But she didn't look up at him—she didn't dare. She had fallen into that trap too many times in the past. . .!

She swallowed past the constriction in her throat and stood up abruptly to walk away from him, towards the window. 'No doubt Jacqueline's simply gone back to pack—so that she can come back and move in here!' she declared unsteadily, and heard his hiss of frustration from behind her.

'Don't you listen, Helen—or do you only hear what you want to hear?' he muttered angrily. 'I said Jackie had offered to buy the Lodge—I didn't say I'd sell it to her! Anyhow, wasn't it you who told me how much Gerald had struggled to keep the estate together——?'

'You're splitting hairs!' she interrupted bleakly. 'Either way, Jacqueline's still at the London house.'

'Oh, yes, she's at the London house!' he stated caustically. 'Packing her things to get out of my life once and for all—because that was the deal I made with her last night!'

She swung back to face him, her eyes wide, vulnerably dark. 'You made a deal?'

'You think you know why Jackie came down here this weekend, Helen, but believe me, you don't know the half of it!' he continued harshly. 'You have no idea of her *real* reasons—of her involvement with Sayton's Folly!'

'*Her* involvement?' She was incredulous now, and his mouth twisted.

'Who do you think told me about Gerald's illness? I already had my suspicions, but they were drastically confirmed that day you showed me the letter from the London solicitors!' He paced away from her, running angry fingers through his hair. 'My Lord, she never could resist prying into my affairs—family affairs!'

'But—but she is family, isn't she?' Helen pointed out desolately, and now he swung back to face her, his mouth a hard, grim line.

'We're separated, Helen—or had you forgotten?' he demanded bitterly. 'Jackie may live at the London house—but that's only because I allowed her to stay on for a short period after her father died. He left his affairs in a terrible mess and she's had to wait a while for her inheritance—and our divorce. Besides, I'm never there anyway—I seem to remember telling you that I spend most of my time abroad. So you see, Helen, we certainly don't *share* the house, as Jackie put it! Besides, I don't like the place. I never have. It has too many memories of my father—but Jackie has no such sensibilities!' he added grimly. 'When Mr Winstanley wrote to me there to tell me that Gerald was dying, Jackie couldn't wait to tell me that I was in line for yet another inheritance! She even came to France to tell me about it! She thought it was just what she needed to sweeten me into being a little more— amenable.'

'So there was talk of a reconciliation!' Helen accused in a brittle voice, and he gave a mirthless smile.

'Oh, I admit she wanted me back!' he muttered tautly. 'She wanted the prestige of being a Sayton again, of having all that money and, now that her father's dead, of being a majority shareholder in the firm, so that she could queen it over the board—only up until now I'd refused to play her little game! I insisted on writing to the London solicitors for news of Gerald, and she returned to London in a temper. I didn't hear anything from the solicitors, so I came back myself—and that was why I was in such a foul mood that night I arrived at Sayton's Folly. I'd flown into London that afternoon, only to learn from Charles that Gerald was already dead—and that Jackie had told him I'd given her permission to handle everything with the solicitors!'

'So that was why you didn't know anything about my mother's death—and about me and Jamie?' Helen queried, dawning understanding in her voice, and he nodded grimly.

'Of course, I didn't realise then just *how* Jackie had handled everything!' He paced restlessly to the hearth, his face dark with anger. 'She played us off one against

the other, Helen,' he declared. 'She knew if I ever
married again she'd have to support her luxury lifestyle
in London herself—and lose any chance she might
have of replenishing her shares in the firm—so she
cold-bloodedly charmed the solicitors into evicting you
from the Lodge, in the hope that you'd be away from
here long before I returned from France!'

'But she must have known that I'd think you'd sent
that letter!' Helen exclaimed, and now he turned back
to face her, his jaw hard and set.

'I can't forgive the way she's treated you, Helen,' he
muttered tautly, 'or the way she's tried to manipulate
me! I gave her an ultimatum: instead of selling her the
Lodge or arguing over a settlement, I'd sell her some
of my shares and give her the money from the sale of
the London house—on condition she gets out of my
life! And so that she can't renege on her word, Charles
has instructions to contact the estate agents first thing
in the morning and put the house on the market!'

Helen could only stare at him now. 'You're *selling*
the London house?'

He smiled grimly. 'Jackie has got what she wanted
after all—but not quite in the way she expected it!'
And he came to stand in front of her then, his eyes
penetratingly dark as they met hers. 'I told you my life
in London was over, Helen, and I'll do anything I can
to prove it to you—to prove that my marriage to
Jackie is over, and has been for a long time!'

'But what will you do?' she stammered, and he
raised his shoulders in a brief shrug.

'I still have my painting, and I can do that here, at
Sayton's Folly. As to whether I stay here or not——'
he paused, his eyes still on her face '—that depends
on you, Helen.'

'Me? Don't you mean Jamie?' It was impossible to

meet his look any longer and she swung away from him, running unsteady fingers through her hair. 'Oh, I know you can give him far more than I ever could!' she got out. 'But I love him, Martyn. He's all I've got!'

'You could have so much more, Helen.'

'I'm not like Jacqueline!' she retorted in a strained voice. 'I don't want your money—or your pity!'

'Is that what you think I'm offering?'

She swallowed painfully. 'What else? You want your son, Martyn, you've made that very clear!'

'And you think I could bring him up alone—without you there, as my wife?' And his hands came out to her shoulders then, turning her back round to face him. 'For heaven's sake, Helen, why do you think I wanted to take you up to the Folly last night?' His voice was husky now. 'I had it all planned—I would even have gone down on bended knee if that was what you wanted!'

'Last night?' she repeated in a dazed voice. 'But I thought that it was the portrait of Jamie!'

'That was part of it, yes,' he told her softly. 'But there was something else too, something I asked Charles to bring from London for me——' And as he spoke he released her to walk back into the hall, reappearing a moment later with a large, dusty brown paper parcel. 'This is for you, Helen. My wedding gift, if you like.'

'Your *wedding* gift?' she echoed, and now she stared at him in bewildered surprise.

He balanced it on the sofa. 'Open it,' he told her huskily, and slowly she began to tear off the wrapping. It was a portrait, but completely different from the portrait of Jamie. It was a young girl lying on a couch, a drift of chiffon against her soft skin. The eyes were the eyes of a girl in love, full of excitement and passion, and the face looking out at Helen was—her own!

'Remember this?' Martyn stood beside her now, watching her face. 'It's the portrait I did of you nine years ago.'

'But I didn't think it was ever finished!' she gasped, unable to look away from it.

'It wasn't, until about five years ago. It was only then that I could bring myself to complete it, and since then it's been locked away in my studio in the London house. Charles hasn't seen this, of course,' he added. 'No one has, except Jackie—but then, she never could resist prying into things that didn't concern her. . .' His lips brushed her hair. 'She was jealous of it—of you. She knew it represented something precious to me. . .'

'So *that* was why she came down here this weekend!' Helen exclaimed, and turned to him then, looking up at him and placing her hands against his chest in a gesture almost of appeal. 'Martyn, believe me, I never told her about Jamie,' she got out in a voice barely above a whisper. 'She must have put two and two together.'

'I realised that. Even though I was so angry, I knew that if you hadn't told me, you sure as hell wouldn't have told Jackie!' he reasoned with a wry twist of his lips. 'She thought that, if all else failed, she could use Jamie to split us apart again—little realising that she was giving me the one thing I wanted, the one thing I knew would bind us together.' His arms slid round her, holding her against him. 'I was angry last night, Helen, bloody angry! But when I calmed down I realised what a godsend it was for me—for *both* of us! I love you, Helen,' he added passionately. 'I need you with me—and I can't take the risk of your disappearing

out of my life a second time!' His mouth came down
on hers then, fiercely passionate, and she was crushed
against him in a breathless embrace, then his fingers
came up to tangle in her hair, and the look in his eyes
was a look she had never thought to see there again.

'Say you'll marry me, Helen,' he breathed
unsteadily.

She smiled then. 'Do you have to ask?' she murmured softly. 'Of course, I'll have to consult a third
party——'

'Jamie!' He smiled, and his mouth came back to
hers in a hard, possessive kiss. 'We'll consult our son
together, Helen,' he said thickly after a moment. 'But
I don't expect any objections from that quarter! Of
course, he'll have to get used to the idea that he won't
be our only son,' he added, 'and he'll have to get used
to being a Sayton!'

'As long as he doesn't turn out like his grandfather—
or his great-uncle!' Helen grinned into his neck. 'And
that reminds me—I have something for you too. I
found it just now, in Mother's box. . .' And she
reached down to pick up the envelope she had discovered earlier. 'It's Gerald's writing,' she told him
gently. 'I think you should be the one to open it.'

He turned the envelope over in his hands, then sank
on to the sofa, pulling her down with him to sit on his
lap. The envelope contained nothing more than a
couple of sheets of paper, completely covered in that
faint, spidery writing, but Martyn began to read, and
a stunned look came into his eyes.

'Good grief—it's Gerald's will!' he got out in a
hoarse voice. He read it through. '*Heavens!*'

'What is it?' Helen demanded, and he turned to
look at her with incredulous eyes.

'He's left me the Folly after all!' he exclaimed in

stunned disbelief. 'But that's not all—Helen, he's left the Lodge to Sarah—and to you!'

'*To me?*' Helen took the sheets of paper from him to read quickly through the familiar writing.

'So my mother was right after all,' she whispered faintly.

'He must have given it to Sarah to look after,' Martyn declared, his voice vibrant with emotion. 'And why not? She was the one person he trusted!'

'He trusted you too, Martyn,' she whispered unsteadily. 'That's why he's left you the one thing he loved—the one thing he knew you would take care of——'

'And not just the Folly either, Helen,' he said softly, and his eyes came back to hers then, and their brilliance almost took her breath away. 'He must have known it would bring us back together. The old devil was determined to keep the estate in the family after all!'

4 FREE

Romances
and 2 Free gifts
-just for you!

Now you can enjoy all the heartwarming emotions of true love for FREE! Discover the uncertainties and the heartbreak, the emotions and tenderness of the modern relationships found in Mills & Boon Romances.

We'll send you 4 captivating Romances as a free gift from Mills & Boon, plus the chance to have 6 Romances delivered to your door every single month.

Claim your FREE books and gifts overleaf.

An irresistible offer from Mills & Boon

Here's a personal invitation from Mills & Boon Reader Service, to become a regular reader of romance. To welcome you, we'd like you to have four books, a CUDDLY TEDDY and a special MYSTERY GIFT absolutely FREE.

Then each month you could look forward to receiving 6 more Brand New Romances, delivered to your door, post and packing free! Plus our Free newsletter featuring author news, competitions and special offers.

This invitation comes with no strings attached. You can cancel or suspend your subscription at any time, and still keep your free books and gifts.

Its so easy. Send no money now. Simply fill in the coupon below and post it to - **Mills & Boon Reader Service, FREEPOST, PO Box 236, Croydon, Surrey CR9 9EL**

NO STAMP REQUIRED

Free Books Coupon

YES! Please rush me my 4 Free Romances and 2 Free Gifts! Please also reserve me a Reader Service Subscription. If I decide to subscribe I can look forward to receiving 6 brand new Romances each month for just £8.70 delivered direct to my door, post and packing is free. If I choose not to subscribe I shall write to you within 10 days - I can keep the books and gifts whatever I decide. I can cancel or suspend my subscription at any time. I am over 18.

Name Mrs/Miss/Ms/Mr _____ EP87R

Address _____

_____ Postcode _____

Signature _____

The right is reserved to refuse an application and change the terms of this offer. Offer expires December 31st 1990. Readers in Southern Africa write to Independent Book Services Pty., Post Bag X3010, Randburg 2125, S.A. Other Overseas and Eire send for details. You may be mailed with other offers from Mills & Boon and other companies as a result of this application. If you would prefer not to share in this opportunity please tick box ☐

Accept 4 Free Romances and 2 Free gifts

• FROM MILLS & BOON •

An irresistible invitation from Mills & Boon Reader Service. Please accept our offer of 4 free romances, a CUDDLY TEDDY and a special MYSTERY GIFT... Then, if you choose, go on to enjoy 6 more exciting Romances every month for just £1.45 each postage and packing free. Plus our FREE newsletter with author news, competitions and much more.

Send the coupon below at once to: Reader Service, FREEPOST, P.O. Box 236, Croydon, Surrey CR9 9EL

✂ — — — — — — | NO STAMP NEEDED | — — — — — — ✂

YES! Please rush me my 4 Free Romances and 2 FREE Gifts! Please also reserve me a Reader Service Subscription so I can look forward to receiving 6 Brand New Romances each month for just £8.70, post and packing free. If I choose not to subscribe I shall write to you within 10 days. I understand I can keep the free books and gifts whatever I decide. I can cancel or suspend my subscription at any time. I am over 18 years of age.

Name Mr/Mrs/Miss _____ EP86R

Address _____

_____

_____ Postcode _____

Signature _____